BOOK 2

PATTERNS IN SPELLING

Patterns with Long Vowels

TIM BROWN

DEBORAH F. KNIGHT

NEW READERS PRESS

Publishing Division of Laubach Literacy International

Syracuse, New York

About the Authors

Deborah Knight began her teaching career in the early 1970s and has taught both reading and English in urban, suburban, and rural settings. Since 1984, Ms. Knight has served as the Coordinator of the Learning Disabilities Assistance Program at Onondaga Community College in Syracuse, New York. Working closely with these OCC students, she has helped them to develop strategies for improving their reading, writing, spelling, and study skills.

Tim Brown has worked with developing and remedial readers and writers since 1978. He teaches courses in spelling as well as freshman composition and literature at Onondaga Community College. He also serves as Senior Professional Tutor at the college's Writing Skills Center, where he has a special interest in teaching spelling to developing and remedial writers and ESL students.

ON THE COVER: A quilt entitled *Rhythm/Color: Morris Men*, 99½" x 99½", by Michael James. This work of art appeared in *The Art Quilt* exhibit and book of the same name. It is reproduced here through the courtesy of The Quilt Digest Press.

ISBN 0-88336-102-7

© 1990

New Readers Press
Publishing Division of Laubach Literacy International
Box 131, Syracuse, New York 13210

Printed in the United States of America

Project Editor: Christina M. Jagger
Manuscript Editor: Mary Hutchison
Illustrations by Larry Raymond
Cover by Chris Steenwerth
Composition by Anne Hyde

9 8 7 6 5 4

Table of Contents

Lesson 1

The Word Families *ake*, *ame*, *ade*, *ate*, and *ape*

Word Families

❶ Listening

ake

Listen to the sound *ake* makes in these words.

cake	take	wake	shake
bake	stake	awake	brake
baker	mistake	snake	brake fluid

ame

Listen to the sound *ame* makes in these words.

name	came	blame	frame
same	became	flame	framed

ade

Listen to the sound *ade* makes in these words.

made	shade	grade	parade
wade	spade	trade	lemonade

ate

Listen to the sound *ate* makes in these words.

ate	late	plate	fascinate
fate	later	state	exaggerate
gate	lately	locate	United States

ape

Listen to the sound *ape* makes in these words.

cape	drape	tape	scrape
escape	grape	shape	scraper

2 **Writing Words.** On the lines below, write the words that you hear.

1. _____   4. _____   7. _____

2. _____   5. _____   8. _____

3. _____   6. _____   9. _____

3 **Dictionary Skills: Alphabetizing.** On the lines below, alphabetize the words in Exercise 2.

1. _____   4. _____   7. _____

2. _____   5. _____   8. _____

3. _____   6. _____   9. _____

4 **Using Sight Words.** Fill in the missing months in this well-known saying.

Thirty days have September, _____, _____, and November. All the

rest have 31 except _____, which has 28.

5 **Finding a Pattern.** The long vowel sounds are the same as the names of the vowels. For example, the long *a* sound is the same as the letter *a*. Listen to the sound the *a* makes in the pairs of words below. In each pair, underline the word that has the long *a* sound. Then put a long vowel mark (‾) over the long *a* in each word you underlined.

1. at   ate   4. Sam   same   7. fate   fat

2. mad   made   5. rate   rat   8. tap   tape

3. hate   hat   6. cap   cape   9. glade   glad

What is the final letter in all the words that have the long *a* sound? _____

Can you hear the final letter in the long *a* words? _____

    Pattern: Words with a long vowel sound often end with a silent *e*.

6 **Adding -ed and -ing to Verbs.** We add -ed to regular verbs (action words) to show action which happened in the past. We add -ing to show action which goes on over a period of time. When a word ends in a silent e, the final e is dropped before adding -ed or -ing. Add -ed and -ing to the verbs below. The first one has been done to get you started.

Verb	-ed	-ing
1. trade	traded	trading
2. name		
3. brake		
4. tape		
5. state		

7 **Finding Another Pattern.** In Exercise 5 you learned that the final silent e is dropped from a word when -ed or -ing is added to it.

Fill in the blanks in the chart below to discover the rest of this pattern. The first one has been done to get you started.

Word	Root	Ending	Was e Dropped?
1. wading	wade	ing	yes
2. paved			
3. saving			
4. shaker			
5. traded			
6. shapeless			
7. safety			
8. games			
9. paleness			
10. pavement			

Silent *e* Pattern 1. Look at the endings in Exercise 7 and fill in the missing words below to state a pattern.

The silent *e* at the end of a word is dropped when we add an ending starting with a

_____.
 (consonant *or* vowel)

The silent *e* is not dropped if the ending starts with a _____.
                                                                            (consonant *or* vowel)

 Using Words. Fill in the blanks in the story with one of the words below. Use each word only once.

ate	cake	lemonade	shade
awake	games	paper	state
baked	later	parade	waded

    After the _____, the Slade family went to the _____ park for a

picnic. They found a table in the _____ and unpacked the food and

_____ plates. The children _____ in the stream and played

_____ until it was time to eat. They _____ hot dogs, salad, and a

_____ that Mrs. Slade had _____ the day before. They also had

_____ to drink. _____, as darkness fell, the children who were

still _____ watched a fireworks display.

Writing Sentences. On the lines below, write the sentences that you hear.

1. _____

2. _____

3. _____

4. _____

5. _____

6. _____

Lesson 2

The Word Families *ane*, *ale*, *ave*, *afe*, and *age*

Sight Words		
July	September	November
August	October	December

Word Families

❶ Listening

ane

Listen to the sound *ane* makes in these words.

cane	vane	lane
Jane	sane	plane
mane	insane	airplane

ale

Listen to the sound *ale* makes in these words.

ale	scale	male
pale	sale	female
tale	salesperson	inhale

ave

Listen to the sound *ave* makes in these words.

cave	pave	brave	behave
gave	save	grave	forgave

afe

Listen to the sound *afe* makes in these words.

safe	safety	safely	chafe

age

Listen to the sound *age* makes in these words.

cage	age	page	engage
wage	teenager	stage	engagement

2 **Writing Words.** On the lines below, write the words that you hear.

1. _____   5. _____   9. _____

2. _____   6. _____   10. _____

3. _____   7. _____   11. _____

4. _____   8. _____   12. _____

3 **Using Sight Words.** Fill in the correct months in the sentences below. Use each of the 12 months once.

1. The United States celebrates its birthday in _____.

2. The shortest month is _____.

3. Yom Kippur is observed in September or _____.

4. Memorial Day is celebrated in _____.

5. Spring arrives in _____.

6. Christmas is celebrated in _____.

7. Martin Luther King's birthday is celebrated in _____.

8. Thanksgiving is celebrated in _____.

9. Labor Day is celebrated in _____.

10. _____ is the last full month of summer.

11. _____ is considered the wedding month.

12. Income tax must be paid by the 15th of _____.

4 **Dictionary Skills: Abbreviations.** Write the abbreviations for the following months on the lines provided. Use your dictionary if necessary.

1. January _____   4. April _____   7. October _____

2. February _____   5. August _____   8. November _____

3. March _____   6. September _____   9. December _____

5 **Dictionary Skills: Irregular Verbs.** Some verbs (action words) do not have *-ed* added to show past time. If a verb does not have *-ed* added to show past time, it is called an irregular verb. The dictionary will usually list the past tense of irregular verbs after the listing for the present tense. Look at the examples below.

come (kŭm) *v.* **came** (kām), **come, com·ing.**

eat (ēt) *v.* **ate** (āt), **eat·en** (ēt′n), **eat·ing.**

The main entry is the present tense form of the verb. The second word is its past tense. The third word is the *past participle*, which is the form used with *have, has,* or *had.* The fourth word is the *present participle*, which is the *-ing* form of the verb.

Below are examples of how these different forms are used in sentences.

1. Please *come* over and *eat* pizza with us.   (Present Tense)
2. Jake *came* over and *ate* with us last night.   (Past Tense)
3. He has *eaten* with us many times.   (Past Participle)
4. We have *eaten* together every Friday.   (Past Participle)
5. Jane had *eaten* with us once or twice.   (Past Participle)
6. I am *coming* over tonight.   (Present Participle)
7. You are *coming* with us, aren't you?   (Present Participle)
8. She is *coming* with us tonight.   (Present Participle)
9. He was *coming* to visit us.   (Present Participle)
10. They were *coming* to see the play.   (Present Participle)

Look up the following irregular verbs in the dictionary and write the different forms on the lines provided. The first one has been done to get you started.

Present Tense	Past Tense	*Have, Has,* or *Had* + Verb	*-ing* Form of Verb
1. make	made	made	making
2. shake			
3. become			
4. take			
5. wake			
6. give			

6 **Writing Dates.** Here are three different ways to write the same date.

December 1, 1992   Dec. 1, 1992   12/1/92

Write each of the following dates in two other ways on the lines provided.

1. October 2, 1994   _____   _____

2. Feb. 4, 1989   _____   _____

3. 4/21/59   _____   _____

4. January 3, 1951   _____   _____

5. Sept. 7, 1990   _____   _____

6. 11/12/66   _____   _____

7 **Reviewing a Pattern.** Underline each word below that has a long *a* sound. Then make the long vowel mark (¯) over each long *a*.

cap	vane	brave	glad	grade	pale	tap
scale	man	cape	van	ape	late	Jane
wade	Brad	mad	tape	Jan	parade	trade

C is a symbol which stands for any consonant. **V** stands for any vowel. Fill in the blank below to restate the pattern learned in Lesson 1.

Pattern: Words that end with aCe usually have a _____ *a* sound.
(long *or* short)

8 **Writing Sentences.** On the lines below, write the sentences that you hear.

1. _____

2. _____

3. _____

4. _____

5. _____

6. _____

Lesson 3

The Word Families *ase, ace, aze, ange,* and *aste*

Sight Words

north	east	south	west
northern	eastern	southern	western

Word Families

① Listening

ase

Listen to the sound *ase* makes in these words.

base	case	vase
basement	chase	eraser

ace

Listen to the sound *ace* makes in these words.

face	lace	pace	race
space	place	graceful	bracelet
trace	misplace	disgrace	

aze

Listen to the sound *aze* makes in these words.

daze	haze	blaze	amaze
gaze	maze	craze	amazement

ange

Listen to the sound *ange* makes in these words.

range	change	strange	danger
arrange	exchange	stranger	dangerous

aste

Listen to the sound *aste* makes in these words.

haste	paste	taste	waste

2 Writing Words. On the lines below, write the words that you hear.

1. _____   5. _____   9. _____

2. _____   6. _____   10. _____

3. _____   7. _____   11. _____

4. _____   8. _____   12. _____

3 Using Sight Words. When the sight words in this lesson are used to indicate a direction, they are not capitalized. However, when they are used in geographical names, such as the names of cities, states, countries, continents, or parts of the world, they are usually capitalized. Study the examples below.

a *north* wind   *North* Dakota
the *east* side of town   *East* Africa
southern hospitality   the *South* Pacific
the *western* frontier   *Western* Sahara

Now fill in the blanks in the sentences below with one of the sight words from this lesson. Use capital letters when necessary.

1. The sun rises in the _____ and sets in the _____.

2. Herds of buffalo used to roam the _____ states.

3. Mexico is _____ of the Texas border.

4. Asia is often called "the Far _____."

5. Alabama and Georgia are _____ states.

6. Massachusetts is on the _____ seaboard.

7. Canada is _____ of the United States.

8. The _____ Hemisphere is north of the equator.

9. There was a wall dividing East and _____ Berlin.

10. The Civil War was fought between the _____ and the _____.

4 **Reviewing a Pattern.** In Lesson 1 you discovered that the final silent *e* is dropped when an ending starting with a vowel is added. The silent *e* is not dropped if the ending starts with a consonant. Add the endings above the columns to each of the root words listed below.

Root Word	-ed	-ing	-s	-less
1. name	_____	_____	_____	_____
2. face	_____	_____	_____	_____
3. flame	_____	_____	_____	_____
4. base	_____	_____	_____	_____
5. blame	_____	_____	_____	_____
6. taste	_____	_____	_____	_____
7. shape	_____	_____	_____	_____
8. age	_____	_____	_____	_____

5 **The Word Families *ace* and *ase*.** Write each word your teacher dictates in the correct column below.

ace	ase
1. _____	1. _____
2. _____	2. _____
3. _____	3. _____
4. _____	4. _____
5. _____	5. _____

Because the *ace* and *ase* family words rhyme, you will need to remember if the /s/ sound in a word is made by *c* or *s*. The *ace* spelling is more common. The five words you just wrote in the *ase* column are the most common words spelled with *ase*. To help you remember them, try to make up a sentence or a rhyme which uses all five words.

6 **Creating Sentences.** On a separate piece of paper, write five sentences about the picture below. Think about what the occasion is, what is happening in the picture, what each person is concerned about, and how things may end up. Use some of the following long *a* words in your sentences.

bake	came	chase	made
baker	place	danger	save
cake	vase	dangerous	safe
plate	arrange	amazement	safely

7 **Writing Sentences.** On the lines below, write the sentences that you hear.

1. _____

2. _____

3. _____

4. _____

5. _____

6. _____

7. _____

8. _____

Lesson 4

The Word Families *ail*, *aim*, *ain*, and *ait*

Sight Words			
people	talk	lose	loose
person	walk	find	tight

Word Families

① Listening

ail

Listen to the sound *ail* makes in these words.

ail	Gail	rail	tail
fail	pail	railroad	detail
mail	sail	trail	retail
nail	sailor	daily	tailor

aim

Listen to the sound *aim* makes in these words.

aim	claim	maim
aimless	reclaim	

ain

Listen to the sound *ain* makes in these words.

gain	pain	stain	remain
rain	plain	contain	maintain
train	complain	obtain	maintenance
strain	explain	retain	entertainment

ait

Listen to the sound *ait* makes in these words.

wait	waiter	trait	bait

2 **Writing Words.** On the lines below, write the words that you hear.

1. _____   5. _____   9. _____

2. _____   6. _____   10. _____

3. _____   7. _____   11. _____

4. _____   8. _____   12. _____

3 **Word Building.** Add either *ail*, *aim*, *ain*, or *ait* to each of the consonants to make a word.

1. b_____   5. m_____   9. cl_____

2. f_____   6. n_____   10. gr_____

3. g_____   7. r_____   11. pl_____

4. h_____   8. s_____   12. tr_____

4 **Using Sight Words**

Part A. The spellings of the sight words *lose* and *loose* are often confused. One way to tell them apart is to remember that each word has an opposite that has the same number of letters.

1. The opposite of *lose* is *find*. Each word has _____ letters.

2. The opposite of *loose* is *tight*. Each word has _____ letters.

Part B. Write the correct sight word in each blank. Use each word only once.

Eight _____ waited at the bus stop. When the bus came it was so crowded that one _____ decided to _____. The other seven got on even though it was a _____ squeeze. No one could _____ a seat. Two students standing in the aisle began to _____. "Would you check to see that the strap on my backpack isn't too _____?" asked one. The other replied, "Let me tighten it for you. You are about to _____ it."

5 **Finding a Pattern.** In each pair of words, underline the word that has a long vowel sound.

1. man	main	4. pal	pail	7. brain	bran
2. am	aim	5. rain	ran	8. bat	bait
3. plain	plan	6. claim	clam	9. van	vain

What letter has been added in the underlined words to make the *a* long? _____

Where has the letter been added? _____

Can you hear the added letter in the underlined words? _____

What sound does *ai* make in the words above? _____

  Pattern: The letters *ai* usually make the long *a* sound.

6 **Dictionary Skills: Homonyms.** *Homonyms* are words that sound alike. The families *ain* and *ane* and the families *ail* and *ale* have some homonym pairs that can easily be confused. To select the correct spelling, you must know the meaning of the word. A dictionary can help you choose the correct word from a pair of homonyms. Answer the following questions using a dictionary when you need to.

1. Is a boy a *mail* or a *male*? _____

2. Which hurts, a *pain* or a *pane*? _____

3. Which shows the direction of the wind, a *vain* or a *vane*? _____

4. Does a clipper ship have *sails* or *sales*? _____

5. Which flies, a *plain* or a *plane*? _____

6. Is a story a *tail* or a *tale*? _____

7. Does a lion have a *main* or a *mane*? _____

8. Is a light color *pail* or *pale*? _____

9. Which is a drink, *ail* or *ale*? _____

10. Which is icy, *hail* or *hale*? _____

7 **Creating Sentences.** On a separate piece of paper, write a story about these pictures. Use some of the following long *a* words in your sentences.

Gail	wait	later	date
sail	mail	railing	gave
sailor	daily	came	exclaim

Sept. 15   Oct. 2   Dec. 20

8 **Writing Sentences.** On the lines below, write the sentences that you hear.

1. _____

2. _____

3. _____

4. _____

5. _____

6. _____
   _____

Lesson 5

The Word Families *aid*, *air*, *aise*, and *aint*

Sight Words			
waist	add	pretty	every
faith	odd	beauty	direction

Word Families

1 Listening

aid

Listen to the sound *aid* makes in these words.

aid	maid	raid
laid	paid	braid
afraid	prepaid	braided

air

Listen to the sound *air* makes in these words.

air	pair	hair	flair
fair	repair	chair	stairs

aise

Listen to the sound *aise* makes in these words.

raise	appraise	mayonnaise
praise	appraisal	

aint

Listen to the sound *aint* makes in these words.

faint	restraint	acquaint
paint	complaint	acquaintance

2 Writing Words. On the lines below, write the words that you hear.

1. _____
2. _____
3. _____
4. _____

5. _____
6. _____
7. _____
8. _____

9. _____
10. _____
11. _____
12. _____

3 Homonyms: *Waste* and *Waist*. Look up *waste* and *waist* in the dictionary and write their definitions below.

waste _____

waist _____

Now write either *waste* or *waist* in the sentences below.

1. The slacks had patch pockets and a belted _____.

2. Do you know what the saying, Haste makes _____, means?

3. Jane went on a diet and took two inches off her _____.

4. Grace didn't want to _____ any yarn, so she made mittens with what was left.

4 Dictionary Skills: Finding the Correct Spelling. You have learned that there are two common spelling patterns that represent the long *a* sound: aCe and aiC. A dictionary can help you choose the correct spelling for words that end in the sound /āC/.

Each of the words spelled phonetically below contains the long *a* sound. Use the dictionary to find the correct spelling based on the meaning given. Look first for the aCe pattern; then for aiC. When you find the spelling that matches the meaning, write the word in the appropriate column below. The first one has been done to get you started.

Phonetic Spelling	Meaning	aCe	aiC
1. /sān/	having a healthy mind	*Sane*	_____
2. /lō′kāt/	to find where something is	_____	_____
3. /grāp/	a fruit that grows on vines in bunches	_____	_____
4. /rĕ mān′/	to stay in a place	_____	_____
5. /trāl/	a path for hikers	_____	_____
6. /plān/	tool used to make wood smooth	_____	_____
7. /rĕ pār′/	to fix something that was broken	_____	_____
8. /flār/	a natural talent for doing something	_____	_____

5 **Familiar Sayings.** Fill in the blanks in these familiar sayings with the long *a* words below.

gained   hesitates   safe   tale   waste

1. _____ not, want not.

2. Better _____ than sorry.

3. He who _____ is lost.

4. Nothing ventured, nothing _____.

5. That is just an old wives' _____.

Now select one of the sayings above and write what it means in your own words.

_____

_____

_____

_____

6 **Writing Sentences.** On the lines below, write the sentences that you hear.

1. _____

2. _____

3. _____

4. _____

5. _____

6. _____

7. _____

8. _____

7 Creating Sentences. Read the following story.

    Dave and Blain have a shop where they make and repair furniture. Dave is a fine craftsman who enjoys working with his hands, knows the tools of his trade, and appreciates the beauty of wood. Blain has a flair for numbers and is good with people. He manages the business and waits on the customers who come to the shop.

On the lines below, write about what might happen in their shop on an ordinary day. Use some form of each word below in a sentence.

1. chair   _____

                      _____

2. repair   _____

                      _____

3. paint   _____

                      _____

4. flair   _____

                      _____

5. paid   _____

                      _____

6. prepaid   _____

                      _____

7. complaint   _____

                      _____

8. praise   _____

                      _____

Lesson 6

The Word Families *ay*, *are*, *ary*, and *azy*

Sight Words		
very	marry	berry
carry	merry	ferry

Word Families

1 Listening

ay

Listen to the sound *ay* makes in these words.

day	pay	play	way
say	repay	display	away
okay	payday	delay	anyway
stay	payment	portray	highway

are

Listen to the sound *are* makes in these words.

bare	flare	fare	rare
care	share	welfare	silverware

ary

Listen to the sound *ary* makes in these words.

vary	library	literary	primary
scary	voluntary	necessary	secondary
solitary	vocabulary	temporary	imaginary

azy

Listen to the sound *azy* makes in these words.

lazy	hazy	crazy

2 Writing Words. On the lines below, write the words that you hear.

1. _____   5. _____   9. _____

2. _____   6. _____   10. _____

3. _____   7. _____   11. _____

4. _____   8. _____   12. _____

3 Dictionary Skills: Sight Words. Five of the sight words in this lesson have homonyms or words that are almost homonyms. Answer the following questions by choosing the correct spelling based on the context. Use a dictionary to check your answers.

1. Is a type of fruit a *berry* or a *bury*?   _____

2. Do you ask someone to *marry* you or *merry* you?   _____

3. Is a boat that carries things a *fairy* or a *ferry*?   _____

4. When it's below zero, is it *vary* cold or *very* cold?   _____

5. When people are happy, are they *marry* or *merry*?   _____

4 Dictionary Skills: Homonyms. The *air* and *are* families have some homonym pairs. Fill in either *air* or *are* in the sentences below. Use your dictionary when you need to.

1. A h_____ is usually larger than a rabbit.

2. It rained today, but tomorrow should be f_____ and warmer.

3. Gail bought a new p_____ of shoes last weekend.

4. Mrs. Blair told her little girl that it isn't polite to st_____.

5. James seems to have a fl_____ for music.

6. I have an appointment to get my h_____ cut today.

7. Do you remember when bus f_____ was twenty-five cents?

8. To get to Dale's apartment, you have to go up three flights of st_____s.

5 **Word Building.** Add either *ay*, *are*, *ary*, or *azy* to each of the letters below to make a word.

1. b_____   4. l_____   7. cr_____

2. c_____   5. m_____   8. gl_____

3. d_____   6. v_____   9. gr_____

6 **Hearing Syllables.** Write down the number of syllables in each of the words you hear.

1. _____   4. _____   7. _____   10. _____

2. _____   5. _____   8. _____   11. _____

3. _____   6. _____   9. _____   12. _____

7 **Writing Words by Syllables.** Write the words that your teacher dictates one syllable at a time. Then write the whole word.

First Syllable	Second Syllable	Third Syllable	Fourth Syllable	Whole Word
1. _____	_____			_____
2. _____	_____			_____
3. _____	_____			_____
4. _____	_____	_____		_____
5. _____	_____	_____		_____
6. _____	_____	_____		_____
7. _____	_____	_____	_____	_____
8. _____	_____	_____	_____	_____

Challenge word:

_____   _____   _____   _____   _____

8 **Reviewing the Days of the Week.** On the longer lines below, write the names of the days of the week, which you learned as sight words in Book 1. On the shorter lines, write an abbreviation for each day.

1. _____ _____   5. _____ _____

2. _____ _____   6. _____ _____

3. _____ _____   7. _____ _____

4. _____ _____

9 **Creating Sentences.** On the lines below, write a sentence using each of the "day" words given.

1. today _____

2. yesterday _____

3. someday _____

4. birthday _____

5. holiday _____

10 **Writing Sentences.** On the lines below, write the sentences that you hear.

1. _____

2. _____

3. _____

4. _____

5. _____

6. _____

7. _____

8. _____

Review of Unit 1

The Long *a*

1 **Word Building.** Add one of the word families listed below to each of the consonants or blends to make a word. Do not make the same word twice.

ake	*ape*	*afe*	*aze*	*aim*	*air*	*are*
ame	*ane*	*age*	*ange*	*ain*	*aise*	*ary*
ade	*ale*	*ase*	*aste*	*ait*	*aint*	*azy*
ate	*ave*	*ace*	*ail*	*aid*	*ay*	

1. b_____

2. d_____

3. f_____

4. f_____

5. l_____

6. m_____

7. m_____

8. n_____

9. p_____

10. r_____

11. s_____

12. s_____

13. w_____

14. w_____

15. cr_____

16. dr_____

17. fl_____

18. sp_____

2 **Reviewing the Patterns for Spelling Long *a*.** On the lines below, write the words that you hear.

1. _____

2. _____

3. _____

4. _____

5. _____

Five different ways to spell long *a* are used in the words above. Write another word for each of the five spellings for long *a*.

1. aCe _____

2. aiC _____

3. aCCe _____

4. ay _____

5. aCy _____

3 **Reviewing a Pattern.** Fill in the blanks to review Silent *e* Pattern 1.

The silent *e* at the end of a word is dropped when an ending starting with a

_____ is added. The silent *e* is not dropped when the ending

starts with a _____ .

4 **Adding Endings.** Add the endings to the words below. Drop the final
silent *e* when necessary.

1. pave + ment   _____

2. trade + ing   _____

3. plain + ly   _____

4. blame + ed   _____

5. fate + ful   _____

6. late + ness   _____

7. scrape + ing   _____

8. behave + ior   _____

9. grade + ing   _____

10. paint + er   _____

11. shade + ed   _____

12. pain + less   _____

13. save + ing   _____

14. shape + less   _____

15. wait + ing   _____

16. main + ly   _____

17. inhale + ing   _____

18. shake + er   _____

19. care + less   _____

20. wake + ful   _____

5 **Writing Dates.** Write each of the dates below by spelling out the
month. Do not use abbreviations.

1. 1/3/51   _____

2. 12/1/79   _____

3. 5/6/90   _____

4. 8/2/45   _____

5. 2/25/89   _____

6. 9/15/92   _____

7. 10/11/84   _____

8. 3/19/50   _____

9. 4/1/10   _____

10. 7/13/91   _____

11. 11/7/81   _____

12. 6/2/90   _____

6 **Dictionary Skills: Irregular Verbs.** Write the irregular verb forms on the lines provided. Use your dictionary if necessary.

Present Tense	Past Tense	Have, Has, or Had + Verb	-ing Form of Verb
1. take			
2. eat			
3. forgive			
4. say			
5. give			
6. lay			
7. make			
8. repay			
9. become			
10. shake			

7 **Filling out Forms.** Fill out the form on the next page using the following details. You can add other details if you wish.

Imagine that you operate a drill press in a factory. On January 3 there was a fire at the factory which began in the north corner of the large room that contains your drill press. No one was hurt in the fire, but the factory was closed for repairs for three weeks. It is now the first day of the next month, and you have to fill out a report for the insurance agency. The agency is trying to find out what caused the fire and wants to know what you saw. Before you left your drill press you saw:

- a woman run to the fire alarm and yell "Fire"
- a vat of wood stain catch on fire
- smoke quickly fill the room with haze
- a foreman wave his arms wildly at a maintenance man
- the maintenance man hit the sprinkler pipes with a long piece of wood
- water from the sprinkler pipes start to fall
- employees run to the exits on the east side of the building

Insurance Report

Date: _____   Social Security Number: _____-____-_____

Name: _____   Date of Birth: _____
      Last   First   Middle   Mo./Day/Yr.

Address: _____
       Street   Apt. No.

_____
   City   County   State   Zip Code

Phone: _____-____-_____   Signature: _____
   (Area Code)

Description of Incident or Accident (Attach additional paper if necessary.)

_____

_____

_____

_____

_____

_____

_____

_____

_____

_____

_____

_____

8 **Reviewing Homonyms.** Answer the following questions by selecting the spelling that fits the meaning.

1. Does a department store have *sales* or *sails*? _____

2. Can you carry water in a *pale* or a *pail*? _____

3. Does a belt go around your *waste* or your *waist*? _____

4. Does a monkey have a *tale* or a *tail*? _____

5. Is the glass in a window a *pane* or a *pain*? _____

6. Does the postman deliver the *male* or the *mail*? _____

7. Was a failed attempt in *vane* or in *vain*? _____

8. If you are healthy, are you *hale* or *hail*? _____

9. If you are sick, do you *ale* or *ail*? _____

10. Is the charge for a bus ride the *fare* or the *fair*? _____

11. When a fire burns, does it *flare* or *flair*? _____

12. To go up one floor, do you climb the *stares* or the *stairs*? _____

9 **Writing Sentences.** On the lines below, write the sentences that you hear.

1. _____

2. _____

3. _____

4. _____

5. _____

6. _____

7. _____

8. _____

10. Crossword Puzzle. Use the clues below to complete this crossword puzzle. Most of the answers are word family or sight words from Unit 1.

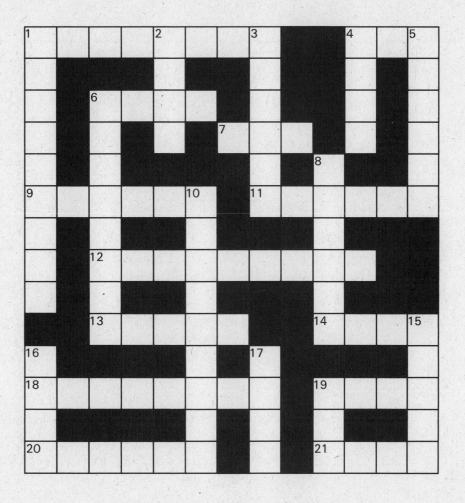

Across

1. The last month
4. Abbreviation for the second month
6. The opposite of succeed
7. Abbreviation for the first month
9. Keep; save; hold onto
11. Recently: Have you seen Jane ___?
12. To attract and hold the interest of someone
13. The opposite of tight
14. Abbreviation for the ninth month
18. The fastest way to travel is by ___.
19. Stages or period of time: the Middle ___
20. To play again
21. The day of the month: What is today's ___?

Down

1. Unsafe: It is ___ to play with matches.
2. What the post office delivers
3. The opposite of wholesale
4. Where your eyes, nose, and mouth are located
5. This is only skin deep.
6. Loyal: My dog is a ___ friend.
8. Fifty of these form the U.S.
10. Required or essential
15. To tell the flavor of
16. Two of a kind: a ___ of shoes
17. The opposite of east
19. The opposite of subtract

Lesson 7

The Word Families *e*, *ee*, and *eer*

Sight Words

move	length	special
prove	strength	especially

Word Families

1 **Listening**

e

Listen to the sound *e* makes in these words.

me	ego	being	legal
be	equal	beyond	react
he	prefix	maybe	senior

ee

Listen to the sound *ee* makes in these words.

bee	tree	three	flee
fee	knee	agree	free
see	needle	coffee	freedom

eer

Listen to the sound *eer* makes in these words.

beer	cheer	pioneer
deer	steer	volunteer

2 **Writing Words.** On the lines below, write the words that you hear.

1. _____   4. _____   7. _____

2. _____   5. _____   8. _____

3. _____   6. _____   9. _____

3 **Types of Syllables.** As you know, a syllable is a part of a word. Each syllable contains one vowel sound. Learning to recognize some of the basic types of syllables found in English words can help you to improve your spelling.

Some words have only one or two syllables, but many others have three or more syllables. We call words that have more than three syllables *polysyllabic words*. Knowing the most common types of syllables can help you to predict the spelling of unfamiliar polysyllabic words.

Remember that **C** stands for any consonant and **V** stands for any vowel. Remember also that the *schwa* (ə) represents the vowel sound in most unaccented syllables. It is the sound made by the first *a* in *afraid*.

Closed Syllables. Most of the words you studied in Book 1 of this series contained closed syllables. To review this type of syllable, write the words that your teacher dictates on the lines below.

1. _____   3. _____   5. _____

2. _____   4. _____   6. _____

Now write **C** above each consonant and **V** above each vowel in the words that you wrote. All of these words are closed syllables.

Closed syllables end with a _____.
                        (consonant *or* vowel)

They have a _____ vowel sound.
              (long *or* short)

Write the words that your teacher dictates on the lines below.

1. _____   3. _____   5. _____

2. _____   4. _____   6. _____

A closed syllable can end in more than one consonant. Pairs of consonants such as *sh* and *ck* which make one sound or blends such as *st* and *nt* can form closed syllables when they follow a short vowel.

Pattern: A closed syllable ends with a short vowel followed by one or more consonants.

Cle Syllables. Cle syllables were also introduced in Book 1. To review Cle syllables, write the words your teacher dictates by syllables. Then write the whole word.

First Syllable	Second Syllable	Whole Word
1. _____	_____	_____
2. _____	_____	_____
3. _____	_____	_____

Look at the second syllable in each word. Each one ends in a consonant plus *le*. Say the second syllable of each of the words above. As you learned in Book 1 of this series, the Cle syllable is usually pronounced /Cə l/.

Cle syllables usually come at the _____ of a word.
(beginning *or* end)

    Pattern: A Cle syllable contains a consonant plus *le* and usually comes at the end of a word.

VCe Syllables. VCe syllables were introduced in Unit 1 of this book. On the lines below, write the words that your teacher dictates.

1. _____	3. _____	5. _____
2. _____	4. _____	6. _____

What is the final letter in each of these words? _____

Does the final letter make a sound? _____

What does the final *e* do to the sound of the vowel before the consonant?

_____

The words you wrote are all VCe syllables. They contain a vowel, a consonant, and a silent *e*. The silent *e* makes the vowel long.

    Pattern: A VCe syllable has a long vowel followed by a consonant and ends in a silent *e*.

Open Syllables. To learn about open syllables, write the words your teacher dictates by syllables. Then write the whole word.

First Syllable	Second Syllable	Whole Word
1. _____		_____
2. _____	_____	_____
3. _____	_____	_____
4. _____	_____	_____
5. _____	_____	_____

The first syllable in each of the words that you wrote is an open syllable. Look at the first syllable in each of the words.

Does the first syllable end in a consonant or a vowel? _____

Is the vowel long or short? _____

Pattern: An open syllable ends in a vowel that is usually long.

4 **Review of Syllable Types.** Write one syllable of each type that you have just learned.

1. Closed _____   3. **VCe** _____

2. Cle _____   4. Open _____

5 **Writing Sentences.** On the lines below, write the sentences that you hear.

1. _____
2. _____
3. _____
4. _____
5. _____
6. _____

Lesson 8

The Word Families *eek*, *eel*, *eet*, and *eem*

<table>
<tr><th colspan="4">Sight Words</th></tr>
<tr><td>blood</td><td>heart</td><td>calf</td><td>beef</td></tr>
<tr><td>flood</td><td>tongue</td><td>half</td><td>teeth</td></tr>
</table>

Word Families

eek

eel

eet

eem

1 Listening

Listen to the sound *eek* makes in these words.

peek	week	cheek	Greek
seek	weekend	creek	sleek

Listen to the sound *eel* makes in these words.

feel	heel	kneel
peel	wheel	steel

Listen to the sound *eet* makes in these words.

beet	greet	meeting	fleet
feet	sheet	sweet	sleet

Listen to the sound *eem* makes in these words.

seem	esteem	redeem

2 Writing Words. On the lines below, write the words that you hear.

1. _____   5. _____   9. _____

2. _____   6. _____   10. _____

3. _____   7. _____   11. _____

4. _____   8. _____   12. _____

3 **Dictionary Skills: Alphabetizing.** Alphabetize the words in Exercise 2 and write them on the lines below.

1. _____   5. _____   9. _____

2. _____   6. _____   10. _____

3. _____   7. _____   11. _____

4. _____   8. _____   12. _____

4 **Word Building.** Add either *eek, eel, eet*, or *eem* to each of the consonants below to make a word. Do not make the same word twice.

1. b_____   5. p_____   9. cr_____

2. f_____   6. s_____   10. gr_____

3. f_____   7. s_____   11. sh_____

4. m_____   8. w_____   12. sl_____

5 **Reviewing Syllable Types**

Closed Syllables. Here are some words with closed syllables. Closed syllables have a short vowel and end with a consonant. Mark the short vowels with the short vowel mark (˘) and write a **C** beside each closed syllable.

1. pig   3. lap   5. bed

2. lim   it   4. trum   pet   6. nap   kin

A closed syllable has a _____ vowel and ends with a _____.

Open Syllables. Here are some words with open syllables. Open syllables usually end with a long vowel. Mark the long vowels with a long vowel mark (¯) and write an **O** beside each open syllable.

1. she   3. go   5. me

2. e · go   4. be   tween   6. re   deem

An open syllable usually ends with a _____ vowel.

Cle Syllables. Here are some words with **Cle** syllables. These syllables contain a consonant plus *le*. Write **Cle** beside each syllable of this type.

1. bun   dle   3. peo   ple   5. nee   dle

2. lit   tle   4. crum   ble   6. bub   ble

A **Cle** syllable contains a consonant plus _____.

VCe Syllables. Here are some words with **VCe** syllables. **VCe** syllables have a long vowel followed by a consonant and a silent *e*. Mark the long vowels with a long vowel mark (⁻), and write **VCe** beside each syllable of this type.

1. bake   3. pale   5. date

2. mis   place   4. pave   ment   6. base   ball

A **VCe** syllable has a _____ vowel, a consonant, and a _____ *e* at the end of it.

6 **Double Vowel Syllables.** Sometimes two vowels that come together make one sound. For example, two *e*'s together make a long *e* sound. *A* and *i* together make a long *a* sound. Syllables in which two vowels together make one vowel sound are called double vowel syllables.

Here are some words with double vowel syllables. Write **D** beside each syllable which has a double vowel.

1. paid   3. beef   5. ex   plain

2. re   deem   4. main   tain   6. vol   un   teer

     Pattern: A double vowel syllable has two vowels together that make one sound.

7 **Creating Sentences.** On a separate sheet of paper, write a paragraph describing this picture. Think about what is happening in the picture and what may happen soon. Use some of the following long *e* words in your sentences.

committee	three	coffee	seem	agree
meeting	senior	sweet rolls	being	cheer
greet	volunteers	needle	beyond	react

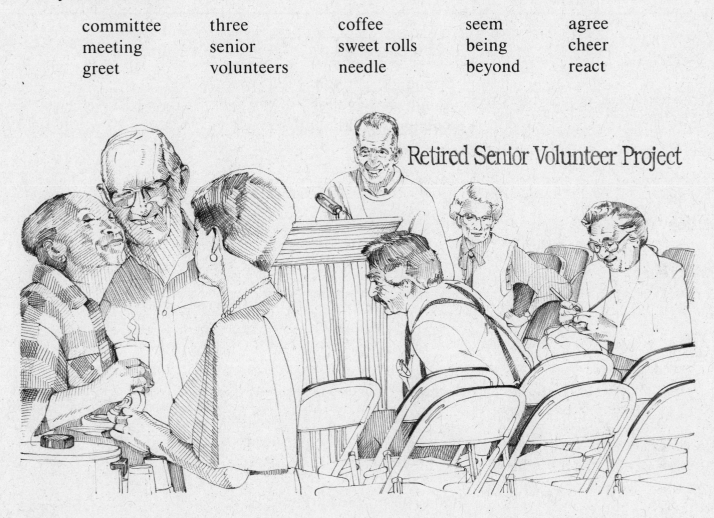

Retired Senior Volunteer Project

8 **Writing Sentences.** On the lines below, write the sentences that you hear.

1. _____

2. _____

3. _____

4. _____

5. _____

6. _____

7. _____

8. _____

Lesson 9

The Word Families *een*, *eed*, *eep*, and *eech*

Sight Words	
rough	dough
tough	though
enough	although

Word Families

① Listening

een

Listen to the sound *een* makes in these words.

seen	teen	thirteen	keen
green	teenager	fourteen	screen
queen	between	fifteen	canteen

eed

Listen to the sound *eed* makes in these words.

feed	weed	speed	bleed
need	deed	succeed	greed
seed	indeed	proceed	agreed

eep

Listen to the sound *eep* makes in these words.

sheep	deep	jeep	weep
sleep	keep	peep	sweep
asleep	doorkeeper	creep	steep

eech

Listen to the sound *eech* makes in these words.

speech	speechless	screech

② Writing Words. On the lines below, write the words that you hear.

1. _____   4. _____   7. _____

2. _____   5. _____   8. _____

3. _____   6. _____   9. _____

Using Sight Words. Write one of the sight words from this lesson in each blank in the sentences below.

1. My cat's tongue is so _____ it feels like sandpaper.

2. Before Jane could bake the bread, she had to let the _____ rise.

3. Slow cooking in a spicy sauce can make _____ meat more tender.

4. It was warm and sunny all day, even _____ the weatherman predicted rain.

5. _____ some unexpected guests came to the party, there was _____ food to go around.

4 **Forming Numbers with _Teen_.** Write the words that your teacher dictates.

1. _____   4. _____   6. _____

2. _____   5. _____   7. _____

3. _____

What pattern is present in all of these words? _____

Pattern: _Teen_ is used to make the numbers thirteen through nineteen.

5 **Reviewing Syllable Types.** The five types of syllables you have studied so far are listed below. An example of each type is given. Write another example of each type of syllable on the lines provided.

Syllable Type	Example	Your Example
1. Closed	set	_____
2. Open	re	_____
3. Cle	ble	_____
4. VCe	ake	_____
5. Double Vowel	eem	_____

6 **Writing Words by Syllables.** Write the words your teacher dictates by syllables. Then write the whole word. Beside each syllable write the syllable type (C for closed, O for open, **Cle**, **VCe**, or D for double vowel).

First Syllable	Second Syllable	Third Syllable	Whole Word
1. _____	_____		_____
2. _____	_____		_____
3. _____	_____		_____
4. _____	_____		_____
5. _____	_____		_____
6. _____	_____	_____	_____
7. _____	_____	_____	_____
8. _____	_____	_____	_____

Challenge word:

_____   _____   _____   _____   _____

7 **Creating Sentences.** Use a form of each of the words below in a sentence. Look up their definitions in a dictionary if necessary.

1. proceed _____

_____

2. fascinate _____

_____

3. fantastic _____

_____

8 **Dictionary Skills: Irregular Verbs.** Look up the following irregular verbs in the dictionary, and write the different forms in the appropriate columns.

Present Tense	Past Tense	*Have, Has,* or *Had* + Verb	*-ing* Form of Verb
1. see	_____	_____	_____
2. feed	_____	_____	_____
3. sleep	_____	_____	_____
4. feel	_____	_____	_____
5. keep	_____	_____	_____

9 **Using Irregular Verbs.** Fill in the blanks in these sentences with the correct form of the verb in parentheses.

1. (feed) Have the dog and cat been _____?

2. (see) Have you _____ my notebook anywhere?

3. (feel) Dean _____ good about the job he had done.

4. (sleep) Last night the baby _____ all through the night.

5. (keep) Jean _____ practicing until she had learned how to type.

10 **Writing Sentences.** On the lines below, write the sentences that you hear.

1. _____

2. _____

3. _____

4. _____

5. _____

6. _____

Lesson 10

The Word Families *ea*, *ead*, *eak*, and *eam*

Sight Words		
oh	coarse	double
owe	course	trouble

Word Families

ea

ead

eak

eam

❶ Listening

Listen to the sound *ea* makes in these words.

sea	tea	pea	eager
season	teaspoon	plea	measles
reason			

Listen to the sound *ead* makes in these words.

bead	plead	read	lead

Listen to the sound *eak* makes in these words.

peak	leak	squeak	creak
speak	weak	streak	sneakers

Listen to the sound *eam* makes in these words.

cream	team	beam	seam
scream	steam	dream	stream

❷ Writing Words. On the lines below, write the words that you hear.

1. _____   4. _____   7. _____

2. _____   5. _____   8. _____

3. _____   6. _____   9. _____

3 Homonyms: *Oh/Owe* and *Coarse/Course*. Read the following sentences and notice how the homonyms are used.

1. *Oh*, how I wish I could finish this job!
2. We *owe* only one more payment on the furniture.

3. This cloth has a *coarse* texture.
4. Steve is taking a *course* at the community college.

Now write one sentence of your own for each of these words.

oh _____

owe _____

coarse _____

course _____

4 Dictionary Skills: Guide Words. Below are pairs of guide words that might be found on dictionary pages. Decide if the words listed below them would appear on the dictionary page that has those guide words. Underline each word that would be found on that page.

1. **flashcube — fledgling**
   flea   flew   flee   feel

2. **pediment — pencil**
   peek   peal   peel   peak

3. **reduce — reflex**
   read   reek   reed   reel

4. **scuffle — seamy**
   seal   seen   screen   seem

5. **teak — Teflon**
   tea   tee   team   teem

6. **we — weave**
   weak   weary   week   weep

5 Dictionary Skills: Homonyms. The long *e* can be spelled many ways. Two spellings of long *e* are *ee* and *ea*. There are many homonym pairs, such as *sea* and *see*, which use both spellings. The correct spelling depends upon the meaning of the word in context. A dictionary can help you choose the correct word from a pair of homonyms. Answer the following questions using a dictionary when you need to.

1. When people run away, do they *flea* or *flee*? _____

2. Is the shore by the *sea* or the *see*? _____

3. Are there seven days in a *weak* or a *week*? _____

4. Is a quick look a *peak* or a *peek*? _____

5. Does a jacket have *seams* or *seems*? _____

6. When it rains very hard, is it *teaming* or *teeming*? _____

7. Is a plant that grows in a marsh a *read* or a *reed*? _____

8. For a soothing drink, would you pour a cup of *tea* or *tee*? _____

6 Word Building. Write either *ee* or *ea* in the blanks in the sentences below. The letters you choose will depend on the meaning of the word in the context of the sentence.

1. Jane felt w___ ___k after her operation.

2. Gail hopes her t___ ___m will win the game.

3. I s___ ___ a fl___ ___ on your cat.

4. To begin a game of golf, you must t___ ___ off.

5. The child p___ ___ked around the corner but wouldn't come in.

6. Can you repair the s___ ___m in my jeans?

7. The back yard is t___ ___ming with insects.

8. I s___ ___m to remember reading something about that.

9. Gene's children asked him to r___ ___d a story to them.

10. The mountain climbers had nearly reached the p___ ___k when night fell.

7 **Writing Words by Syllables.** Write the words that you hear one syllable at a time. Then write the whole word on the line at the right. Use the syllable type to help you spell the word.

First Syllable	Second Syllable	Third Syllable		Whole Word
1. _____	_____			_____
2. _____	_____			_____
3. _____	_____			_____
4. _____	_____			_____
5. _____	_____			_____
6. _____	_____	_____		_____
7. _____	_____	_____		_____
8. _____	_____	_____		_____

Challenge word:

_____   _____   _____   _____   _____   _____

8 **Writing Sentences.** On the lines below, write the sentences that you hear.

1. _____

2. _____

3. _____

4. _____

5. _____

6. _____

7. _____

8. _____

Lesson 11

The Word Families *eat*, *eal*, *ean*, and *eap*

Sight Words			
busy	color	purpose	else
bury	sugar	suppose	wolf

Word Families

1 Listening

eat

Listen to the sound *eat* makes in these words.

eat	heat	neat	cheat
beat	heater	seat	treat
meat	wheat	repeat	defeat

eal

Listen to the sound *eal* makes in these words.

meal	deal	appeal
real	heal	reveal
seal	steal	conceal

ean

Listen to the sound *ean* makes in these words.

bean	Jean	lean
dean	mean	clean

eap

Listen to the sound *eap* makes in these words.

heap	leap	cheap

2 Writing Words. On the lines below, write the words that you hear.

1. _____   4. _____   7. _____

2. _____   5. _____   8. _____

3. _____   6. _____   9. _____

3 **Dictionary Skills: Homonyms.** Below are several more sets of homonyms spelled with *ea* and *ee*. Answer the following questions, using a dictionary to help you select the correct spelling based on the context.

1. Do bells *peal* or *peel*?   _____

2. Is a dark red vegetable a *beat* or a *beet*?   _____

3. Will a cut on your finger *heal* or *heel*?   _____

4. Did the thief *steal* or *steel*?   _____

5. Will you *meat* or *meet* your friend for lunch?   _____

6. Is a remarkable achievement a *feat* or a *feet*?   _____

7. Do baby chicks *cheap* or *cheep*?   _____

8. Does a fishing rod have a *real* or a *reel*?   _____

4 **Word Building.** Write either *ee* or *ea* in the blanks in the sentences below. The letters you choose will depend on the meaning of the word.

1. The Buffalo Bills b__ __t the Pittsburgh Steelers.

2. Did the thief st__ __l anything when he broke into your car?

3. Those peaches will be ch__ __per to buy in a few weeks.

4. The h__ __l of Grace's shoe broke off when she tripped.

5. Steve is a vegetarian, so he never eats m__ __t.

6. Mrs. Blair's f__ __t hurt from so much walking.

7. Jane's dream seemed so r__ __l that it frightened her.

8. Jean has a new set of stainless st__ __l pots and pans.

9. Gary was p__ __ling potatoes in the kitchen when we arrived.

10. Finishing the marathon was a remarkable f__ __t for Lee.

Reviewing Syllable Types. Write each syllable below on a line under the correct heading. The first one has been done to get you started.

✓neer	dle	ro	pip	ble
sep	tic	ne	a	pane
rain	sipe	ple	tane	ceed

Closed

1. _____
2. _____
3. _____

Open

1. _____
2. _____
3. _____

Cle

1. _____
2. _____
3. _____

VCe

1. _____
2. _____
3. _____

Double

1. __neer_____
2. _____
3. _____

 Writing Words by Syllables. Write the words that your teacher dictates one syllable at a time. Then write the whole word.

First Syllable	Second Syllable	Third Syllable	Whole Word
1. _____	_____		_____
2. _____	_____		_____
3. _____	_____		_____
4. _____	_____		_____
5. _____	_____		_____
6. _____	_____	_____	_____
7. _____	_____	_____	_____
8. _____	_____	_____	_____

7 **Creating Sentences.** On a separate sheet of paper, write a paragraph about the picture below. Use some of the following long *e* words in your sentences.

team	leap	lead	speed
cheer	steal	beat	streak
scream	succeed	defeat	season

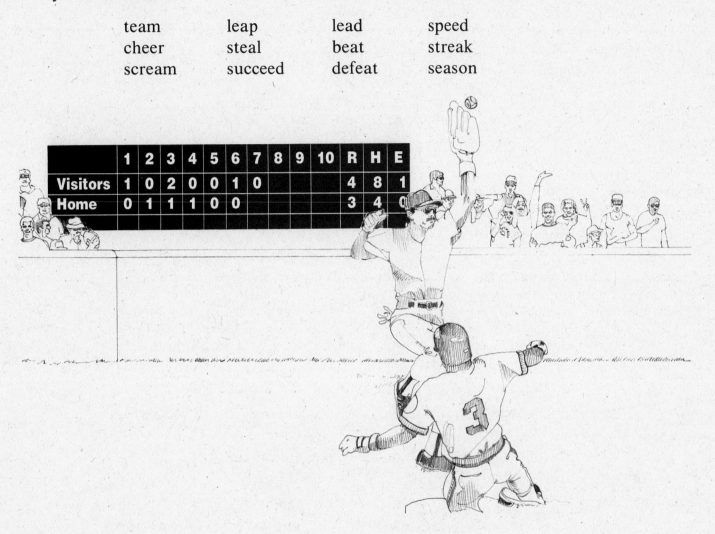

	1	2	3	4	5	6	7	8	9	10	R	H	E
Visitors	1	0	2	0	0	1	0				4	8	1
Home	0	1	1	1	0	0					3	4	0

8 **Writing Sentences.** On the lines below, write the sentences that you hear.

1. _____

2. _____

3. _____

4. _____

5. _____

6. _____

7. _____

8. _____

Lesson 12

The Word Families *each*, *east*, and *ear*

<table>
<tr><td colspan="4" align="center">Sight Words</td></tr>
<tr><td>been</td><td>broad</td><td>clothes</td><td>leaf</td></tr>
<tr><td>many</td><td>machine</td><td>material</td><td>leash</td></tr>
</table>

Word Families

each

1 Listening

Listen to the sound that *each* makes in these words.

each	beach	peach	reach
teach	bleach	impeach	preach
teacher	unbleached	impeachment	

east

Listen to the sound that *east* makes in these words.

| east | beast | feast | least |

ear

Listen to the sound that *ear* makes in these words.

ear	hear	year	weary
dear	near	clear	appear
fear	rear	shears	disappear

2 Writing Words. On the lines below, write the words that you hear.

1. _____   5. _____   9. _____

2. _____   6. _____   10. _____

3. _____   7. _____   11. _____

4. _____   8. _____   12. _____

3 Finding a Pattern

Part A. Write the words that you hear one syllable at a time. Then answer the questions below.

1. _____   _____   4. _____   _____

2. _____   _____   5. _____   _____

3. _____   _____   6. _____   _____

Look at the first syllable of each word you wrote. What type of syllable is the first syllable?

_____

Look at the second syllable of each word you wrote. Does the second syllable begin with a

consonant or a vowel? _____

> **Pattern:** If the first syllable of a two-syllable word is closed, the second syllable usually begins with a consonant.

Part B. When the first syllable ends with the same consonant that the second syllable begins with, you will hear only one consonant sound in the middle of the word. If you do not hear two consonant sounds, the middle consonant is usually doubled.

    Examples: muffin   tennis   sudden

Write the words that you hear one syllable at a time. Then answer the questions below.

1. _____   _____   3. _____   _____

2. _____   _____   4. _____   _____

Do the words you wrote follow the pattern in Part A? _____

Look at the last letter in each first syllable and the first letter in each second syllable. What

do you notice about these letters? _____

> **Pattern:** If the first syllable of a two-syllable word is closed, the second syllable usually begins with a consonant. If you do not hear two consonant sounds, the middle consonant is usually doubled.

Reviewing Syllable Types. Write each syllable below on a line under the correct heading.

ceal	cle	re	nit	tle
sis	son	be	o	pone
site	tain	kle	tine	deed

Closed   **Open**   **Cle**

1. _____   1. _____   1. _____

2. _____   2. _____   2. _____

3. _____   3. _____   3. _____

VCe   **Double**

1. _____   1. _____

2. _____   2. _____

3. _____   3. _____

 Writing Words by Syllables. Write the words that your teacher dictates one syllable at a time. Then write the whole word. Use the syllable types to help you spell the word.

First Syllable	Second Syllable	Third Syllable	Whole Word
1. _____	_____		_____
2. _____	_____		_____
3. _____	_____		_____
4. _____	_____	_____	_____
5. _____	_____	_____	_____
6. _____	_____	_____	_____

Challenge word:

_____ _____ _____ _____   _____

6 **Homonyms:** *Hear* **and** *Here.* Read the following sentences and notice how the homonyms are used.

1. We *hear* with our ears.
2. I can't *hear* what you are saying.

3. *Here* comes my sister now.
4. Bring those boxes over *here*.

In the sentences below, fill in either *hear* or *here*.

1. If you will wait _____, I will be right back.

2. I _____ that James is going to come home.

3. Did you _____ the telephone ring?

4. The wind scattered the leaves _____ and there.

Now write one sentence of your own for each word.

hear _____

here _____

7 **Writing Sentences.** On the lines below, write the sentences that you hear.

1. _____

2. _____

3. _____

4. _____

5. _____

6. _____

7. _____

8. _____

9. _____

10. _____

Lesson 13

The Word Families *eeze*, *ease*, *eave*, and *ceive*

Sight Words		
country	young	cheese
touch	hero	sleeve

Word Families

① Listening

eeze

Listen to the sound *eeze* makes in these words.

breeze   freeze   sneeze   squeeze

ease

Listen to the sounds *ease* makes in these words.

ease   tease   cease   crease
disease   please   grease   decrease
              displease   release   increase

eave

Listen to the sound *eave* makes in these words.

heave   leave   leaves   weave

ceive

Listen to the sound *ceive* makes in these words.

conceive   deceive   receive

② Writing Words. On the lines below, write the words that you hear.

1. _____   4. _____   7. _____

2. _____   5. _____   8. _____

3. _____   6. _____   9. _____

3 **Patterns for Spelling Long *e*.** Write the words that you hear on the lines below.

1. _____   3. _____

2. _____   4. _____

Four different ways to spell long *e* are used in the words above. Now write another word for each of the four spellings for long *e*.

1. e _____   3. ea _____

2. ee _____   4. ei _____

4 **An Uncommon Pattern: eCe.** In Unit 1 you learned many words with the pattern aCe. You learned that a silent *e* at the end of a word makes the *a* long. In this unit you have not learned any eCe words. That is because eCe is not a common spelling for long *e*.

Write the words which your teacher dictates. Each of these is spelled with eCe.

1. _____   3. _____   5. _____

2. _____   4. _____   6. _____

A few other words that contain a long *e* sound follow the **VCe** syllable pattern, but not very many.

    Pattern: Long *e* is spelled eCe in only a few words.

5 **The Root *ceive*.** Several words can be built with the root *ceive*. Look up the words below and write their definitions on the lines provided.

1. receive _____

2. conceive _____

3. deceive _____

6 **Dictionary Skills: Finding the Correct Spelling.** Because there are so many different ways to spell long *e*, sometimes you won't remember which one to use. If you can't remember which spelling of long *e* to use, or if the word is new to you, check your dictionary.

Each of the words spelled phonetically below contains the long *e* sound. Use the dictionary to find the correct spelling based on the meaning given. Look first for the *ea* pattern, then for *ee* and *ei*. When you find the spelling that matches the meaning, write the word on the line to the right.

Phonetic Spelling	Meaning	Correct Spelling
1. /brēz/	a gentle wind	_____
2. /fēst/	a large, elaborate meal	_____
3. /pər sēv/	to become aware of or detect	_____
4. /spēk/	to talk or converse	_____
5. /spēch/	a talk delivered to an audience	_____
6. /sēs/	to come to an end; stop	_____
7. /sēz/	to take suddenly by force; grab	_____
8. /ēʹzē/	needing little effort; not hard	_____
9. /fēʹbəl/	weak; without strength	_____
10. /rĕ sēv/	to take in, acquire, or obtain	_____

Now fill in each word you wrote in the appropriate column below.

ea	*ee*	*ei*
1. _____	1. _____	1. _____
2. _____	2. _____	2. _____
3. _____	3. _____	3. _____
4. _____		

7 **Reviewing a Pattern.** Fill in the blanks below to review Silent *e* Pattern 1.

The silent *e* at the end of a word is dropped when an ending starting with a

_____ is added. The silent *e* is not dropped when the ending starts

with a _____.

8 **Adding Endings.** Add the endings to the words below. Drop the final silent *e* when necessary.

1. displease + ed   _____

2. cease + less   _____

3. sneeze + ing   _____

4. please + ure   _____

5. conceive + able   _____

6. weave + ing   _____

7. deceive + ing   _____

8. disease + ed   _____

9. receive + able   _____

10. grease + less   _____

9 **Writing Sentences.** On the lines below, write the sentences that you hear.

1. _____

2. _____

3. _____

4. _____

5. _____

6. _____

7. _____

8. _____

_____

Lesson 14

The Word Families *ey*, *y*, and *ly*

Sight Words

father	parent	couple
mother	aunt	cousin

Word Families

ey

1 Listening

Listen to the sound that *ey* makes in these words.

key	honey	kidney	jersey
hockey	money	journey	volleyball
monkey	valley		

y

Listen to the sound *y* makes in these words.

any	icy	weary	wavy
shady	greasy	sleepy	bravery
study	greedy	recovery	secretary

ly

Listen to the sound *ly* makes in these words.

jelly	lately	truly	gently
Molly	lonely	daily	doubly
ugly	really		

2 Writing Words. On the lines below, write the words that you hear.

1. _____   5. _____   9. _____

2. _____   6. _____   10. _____

3. _____   7. _____   11. _____

4. _____   8. _____   12. _____

3 **Reviewing a Pattern.** In Lesson 12 you learned that if the first syllable of a two-syllable word is a closed syllable, the second syllable usually begins with a consonant. If you do not hear two consonants in the middle of the word, the middle consonant is usually doubled. Write the words your teacher dictates, following this pattern.

1. _____   3. _____   5. _____

2. _____   4. _____   6. _____

4 **Finding a Pattern.** Look at the following root words and their endings.

Root	Ending	New Word	Root	Ending	New Word
1. marry	+ ed	married	5. cry	+ ing	crying
2. lazy	+ est	laziest	6. copy	+ ing	copying
3. easy	+ ly	easily	7. carry	+ ing	carrying
4. penny	+ less	penniless	8. vary	+ ing	varying

The letter before the final *y* in the root words is a _____.

(consonant *or* vowel)

What happens to the final *y* when the first four endings are added?

_____

What happens to the final *y* when *-ing* is added? _____

   Pattern: When adding a suffix to a word that ends in **C**y, change the *y* to *i* unless the suffix begins with *i*.

5 **Adding Endings to Words That End in y.** Add the endings to the words below.

1. copy + er   _____   6. sorry + er   _____

2. journey + ed _____   7. rainy + est   _____

3. sleepy + ly   _____   8. marry + ing   _____

4. study + ing   _____   9. greedy + ly   _____

5. easy + est   _____   10. jockey + ed   _____

6 **Discovering Another Pattern.** Look at the pairs of singular and plural words below.

Singular	Plural	Singular	Plural	Singular	Plural
cake	cakes	key	keys	baby	babies
team	teams	valley	valleys	penny	pennies

What letter is added to make most words plural? _____

What happens to words that end in a consonant plus *y* when they become plural?

_____

Pattern: To make a word ending in **C***y* plural, change the *y* to *i* and add *-es*.

Following the pattern above, write the plurals of these words.

1. city   _____   4. jelly   _____

2. lily   _____   5. injury   _____

3. puppy   _____   6. mystery   _____

7 **Word Building with -***ly***.** When *-ly* is added to some adjectives (words that describe nouns), the new words that are formed are adverbs (words that describe verbs, adjectives, or other adverbs). Study the examples below.

> The *graceful* couple danced all evening. (*Graceful* is an adjective.)
> The couple danced *gracefully* all evening. (*Gracefully* is an adverb.)

Create adverbs from the adjectives below by adding *-ly* to them.

1. safe   _____   6. hasty   _____

2. easy   _____   7. weary   _____

3. fair   _____   8. lone   _____

4. brave   _____   9. late   _____

5. strange   _____   10. sleepy   _____

8 **Creating Sentences.** On a separate sheet of paper, write a paragraph describing the scene below. Use some of the following family and sight words in your sentences.

father	cousin	journey	hear
mother	couple	reach	clear
parents	yearly	appear	shady
aunt	feast	leave	volleyball

9 **Writing Sentences.** On the lines below, write the sentences that you hear.

1. _____
2. _____
3. _____
4. _____
5. _____
6. _____
7. _____
8. _____

Review of Unit 2

The Long *e*

1 **Reviewing Syllable Types.** You have learned five syllable types in this unit: closed (C), open (O), consonant + *le* (Cle), vowel-consonant-*e* (VCe), and double vowel (D).

Part A. Fill in the blanks below to review the five syllable types.

1. A closed syllable ends with a _____ and has a _____ vowel.

2. An open syllable ends with a _____, which is usually _____.

3. A consonant + *le* syllable (Cle) usually comes at the _____ of a word.

4. The first vowel in a vowel-consonant-*e* syllable (VCe) is _____ and the *e* is _____.

5. A double vowel syllable has _____ vowels together that make _____ sound.

Part B. Place the following syllables under the correct heading.

ain	re	son	cle	dle
ba	sim	tle	reed	ane
com	ade	ite	fe	ceal

Closed	Open	Cle
1. _____	1. _____	1. _____
2. _____	2. _____	2. _____
3. _____	3. _____	3. _____

VCe	Double Vowel
1. _____	1. _____
2. _____	2. _____
3. _____	3. _____

Part C. On the line beside each of the following syllables, write what kind of syllable it is.

1. ple _____
2. gel _____
3. us _____
4. lete _____

5. main _____
6. mu _____
7. ble _____
8. ceed _____

9. e _____
10. ale _____
11. pire _____
12. ba _____

2 **Writing Words by Syllables.** Write the words that you hear one syllable at a time. Then write the whole word on the line at the right.

First Syllable	Second Syllable	Third Syllable	Whole Word
1. _____	_____		_____
2. _____	_____		_____
3. _____	_____	_____	_____
4. _____	_____	_____	_____
5. _____	_____	_____	_____

3 **Patterns for Spelling Long e.** On the lines below, write the words that you hear.

1. _____
2. _____
3. _____
4. _____
5. _____
6. _____

Six different ways to spell long *e* are used in the words you wrote. Now write another word for each of the six spellings for long *e*.

1. e _____
2. ee _____
3. ea _____
4. ey _____
5. y _____
6. eCe _____

4 **Dictionary Skills: Guide Words.** Below are sets of guide words that might be found on dictionary pages. Decide if the words listed below them would appear on the dictionary page that has those guide words. Underline each word that would be found on that page.

1. **headache — hearken**

   hear   heal   here   heel

2. **bear — because**

   beet   bean   been   beat

3. **stay — stencil**

   steal   seam   seem   steel

4. **chatter — cheer**

   cheep   cheek   cheat   cheap

5 **Homonyms.** Write either *ea* or *ee* in the blanks below depending on the definition given. Use your dictionary to check your answers.

1. the opposite of strong   w__ __k

2. a dark red vegetable   b__ __t

3. to listen with the ear   h__ __r

4. to run away   fl__ __

5. a strong metal   st__ __l

6. a group working together   t__ __m

7. return to health   h__ __l

8. authentic   r__ __l

9. the skin of a fruit   p__ __l

10. not expensive   ch__ __p

6 **Word Building.** Add a syllable from Column 2 to a syllable in Column 1 to make a word. Write the new words on the lines provided. Use each syllable only once. The first one has been done to get you started.

Column 1	Column 2	New Word
√be	fee	1. _began_
nee	teen	2. _____
cof	ceed	3. _____
fif	√gan	4. _____
suc	dle	5. _____

7 **Adding Endings.** Add the endings to the words below.

1. sick + ly   _____
2. muddy + est   _____
3. name + less   _____
4. baby + ing   _____
5. parade + ed   _____
6. penny + s *or* es   _____
7. legal + ly   _____
8. happy + ly   _____
9. price + less   _____
10. lazy + ly   _____
11. secret + ly   _____
12. copy + ing   _____
13. dangerous + ly   _____
14. escape + ed   _____
15. silly + er   _____
16. race + ing   _____
17. puppy + s *or* es   _____
18. sudden + ly   _____

8 **Dictionary Skills: Using Words with Many Syllables.** Complete the following sentences by filling in one of the words below. Use your dictionary to find the meanings of the words when you need to.

absolute	confiscated	grapple	mayonnaise	reignite
compensate	established	magnetic	preheat	stagnate

1. That company was _____ in 1901.

2. If a fire isn't completely out, it can _____.

3. How can I _____ you for the fine job you did?

4. Would you like mustard or _____ on your sandwich?

5. The water in the pond will _____ as it dries up.

6. A compass has a _____ needle which points north.

7. The police _____ the illegal weapons.

8. When the electricity went off, the room was in _____ darkness.

9. A meeting was called to _____ with the problem of absenteeism.

10. You should _____ the oven before you start to bake the cake.

9 **Dictionary Skills: Irregular Verbs.** Fill in the blanks in the sentences below with the correct form of the verb in parentheses. Look up the verbs in a dictionary if you need to find the correct form.

1. (leave)   Have all your guests _____ so soon?

2. (weep)   Lee nearly _____ with joy when he won the scholarship.

3. (hear)   Have you _____ from Beatrice lately?

4. (beat)   The volleyball team has been _____ only once this year.

5. (lead)   The guide _____ us down the path to the bottom of the canyon.

6. (mean)   I _____ to tell you about that yesterday, but I forgot.

7. (steal)   Steve has _____ more bases than any other player on the team.

8. (teach)   Mr. Teeter _____ English for twenty-five years.

9. (deal)   Before Eileen _____ the cards, Jean served the dessert.

10. (seek)   The board members have _____ a solution to that problem for weeks.

10 **Writing Sentences.** On the lines below, write the sentences that you hear.

1. _____

2. _____

3. _____

4. _____

5. _____

6. _____

7. _____
   _____

8. _____
   _____

11 **Crossword Puzzle.** Use the clues below to complete the puzzle. Most of the answers are word family or sight words from Unit 2.

Across

1. Dyed; used crayons
4. A loud, shrill cry
8. Opposite of far
10. Particularly: She is ____ good in math.
11. A person who offers free help
14. Is in debt: He ____ me a dollar.
17. Without a kind of sweetener: ____ gum
19. "____, myself, and I"
20. Belonging to him
21. Gets meaning from printed words
22. Not hard

Down

1. To think of or imagine something
2. The opposite of follow
3. Vanish: How could he ____ without a trace?
5. The child of your aunt or uncle
6. Having the same value as something else: Does 1 plus 1 ____ 2?
7. This is used to buy things.
9. Someone older than twelve but younger than twenty
12. An ending meaning "without"
13. These can be found on fishing poles and movie projectors.
15. You and I
16. Full of small pits: These grapes are ____.
18. He, ____, and it
20. The opposite of she

Lesson 15

The Word Families *ime*, *ibe*, *ike*, *ice*, *ipe*, and *ile*

<table>
<tr><td colspan="4" align="center">**Sight Words**</td></tr>
<tr><td>question</td><td>die</td><td>board</td><td>both</td></tr>
<tr><td>answer</td><td>dye</td><td>bored</td><td>rhyme</td></tr>
</table>

Word Families

1 Listening

ime

Listen to the sound *ime* makes in these words.

dime	time	prime
chime	overtime	grime
crime	sometimes	slime

ibe

Listen to the sound *ibe* makes in these words.

bribe	tribe	describe	prescribe

ike

Listen to the sound *ike* makes in these words.

like	bike	dike	spike
alike	hike	Mike	strike

ice

Listen to the sound *ice* makes in these words.

ice	rice	device	slice
mice	price	advice	sacrifice
nice	twice		

ipe

Listen to the sound *ipe* makes in these words.

ripe	wipe	stripe
gripe	swipe	pipeline

ile

Listen to the sound *ile* makes in these words.

file	mile	tile	awhile
pile	smile	while	meanwhile

2 **Writing Words.** On the lines below, write the words that you hear.

1. _____   4. _____   7. _____

2. _____   5. _____   8. _____

3. _____   6. _____   9. _____

3 **Dictionary Skills: Homonyms.** Look up the definitions of the following sight words and write them on the lines.

1. board _____

2. bored _____

3. dye _____

4. die _____

Now write a sentence using a form of each of these words.

1. board _____

2. bored _____

3. dye _____

4. die _____

4 **Syllable Types.** The five types of syllables you have studied so far are listed below. An example of each type is given. Write another example of each type of syllable on the lines provided.

Syllable Type	Example	Your Example
1. Closed	bit	_____
2. Open	li	_____
3. Cle	tle	_____
4. VCe	ime	_____
5. Double Vowel	tain	_____

5 **The VCe Syllable Type.** A vowel-consonant-*e* syllable ends in a silent *e*. This silent *e* usually causes the vowel to be long. On the lines below, write nine words which follow the **VCe** pattern and have a long *i* sound.

1. _____   4. _____   7. _____

2. _____   5. _____   8. _____

3. _____   6. _____   9. _____

6 **Review of Silent *e* Pattern 1.** The silent *e* at the end of a word is dropped when adding an ending that starts with a vowel. When the ending starts with a consonant, the silent *e* is not dropped. Add the endings to the words below.

1. mile + s _____   7. time + less _____

2. tribe + al _____   8. nice + est _____

3. price + less _____   9. smile + ing _____

4. bike + ed _____   10. like + ness _____

5. pipe + ing _____   11. wipe + er _____

6. like + ly _____   12. describe + ed _____

7 **Finding Root Words.** Write the root word for each of the words below.

1. planning _____   7. filed _____

2. striped _____   8. puppies _____

3. bikes _____   9. grimy _____

4. biggest _____   10. hiker _____

5. gushes _____   11. sliced _____

6. smiling _____   12. striking _____

8 **Writing Unfamiliar Names.** On the lines below, write the last names that your teacher dictates. The types of syllables you have studied will help you to spell the names.

1. _____   5. _____   9. _____

2. _____   6. _____   10. _____

3. _____   7. _____   11. _____

4. _____   8. _____   12. _____

9 **Locating Names in a Directory.** Below is a directory of doctors in a physicians' office building. Underline the names from Exercise 8.

Abrams	Bostic	Gale	Miles	Seeley
Aiken	Cadwell	Gilbo	Patrick	Stapleton
Alexander	Case	Hickle	Price	Sullivan
Bailey	Collins	Johnson	Regan	Tassone
Beecher	Deaver	Keene	Riley	Updike
Bidwell	Eaton	Lacy	Romano	Weeks

10 **Writing Sentences.** On the lines below, write the sentences that you hear.

1. _____

2. _____

3. _____

4. _____

5. _____

6. _____

7. _____

8. _____

9. _____

10. _____

Lesson 16

The Word Families *ine*, *ire*, *ide*, *ite*, *ife*, and *ive*

```
                        Sight Words
         cough      route     shoulder
         court      group     thorough
```

Word Families

1 Listening

ine

Listen to the sound *ine* makes in these words.

dine	fine	spine	shine
line	define	whine	sunshine
mine	decline	combine	Valentine

ire

Listen to the sound *ire* makes in these words.

fire	tire	bonfire	admire
hire	entire	inquire	desire
wire	retired	require	expire

ide

Listen to the sound *ide* makes in these words.

hide	beside	ride	tide
side	decide	bride	slide
wide	divide	pride	provide

ite

Listen to the sound *ite* makes in these words.

bite	quite	ignite	excite
kite	unite	invite	excitement
white	write	recite	unexcited

ife

Listen to the sound *ife* makes in these words.

| life | knife | wife | lifetime |

ive

Listen to the sound *ive* makes in these words.

| live | drive | hive |
| alive | driveway | thrive |

2 **Writing Words.** On the lines below, write the words that you hear.

1. _____   4. _____   7. _____

2. _____   5. _____   8. _____

3. _____   6. _____   9. _____

3 **Word Building.** Add *ine, ire, ide, ite, ife,* or *ive* to each of the consonants to make a word. Do not make the same word twice.

1. f_____   4. h_____   7. m_____

2. f_____   5. l_____   8. t_____

3. h_____   6. l_____   9. wr_____

4 **Using Sight Words.** Use one of the sight words from this lesson in each of the following sentences.

1. A large _____ of students was watching the game.

2. Gary's son has had a paper _____ for two years.

3. The doctor gave him a _____ examination.

4. Mary's recent cold left her with a bad _____.

5. Dave injured his _____ and can't pitch today.

6. Mike will meet us at the tennis _____ at five o'clock.

5 **Forming the Plurals of Words That End in *f* or *fe*.** Some words that end in *f* or *fe* are made plural by changing the *f* or *fe* to *v* and adding *-es*. Make these words plural by following this pattern. The first one has been done to get you started.

1. wife   _wives_____   5. half   _____

2. life   _____   6. calf   _____

3. knife   _____   7. self   _____

4. leaf   _____   8. wolf   _____

6 **Word Building.** Use each root word to make three more words by adding three of these endings: *-ed*, *-ment*, *-ing*, *-less*, *-er*, or *-s*. Use each ending at least once.

1. excite _____ _____ _____

2. unite _____ _____ _____

3. time _____ _____ _____

4. retire _____ _____ _____

5. dine _____ _____ _____

6. write _____ _____ _____

7. fine _____ _____ _____

8. wire _____ _____ _____

Now make the two new words below.

1. excite + ed + ly _____   2. decide + ed + ly _____

7 **Dictionary Skills: Irregular Verbs.** Look up the following irregular verbs in the dictionary, and write the different forms in the appropriate columns.

Present Tense	Past Tense	*Have, Has,* or *Had* + Verb	*-ing* Form of Verb
1. ride	_____	_____	_____
2. strike	_____	_____	_____
3. bite	_____	_____	_____
4. write	_____	_____	_____
5. hide	_____	_____	_____
6. drive	_____	_____	_____

8 Creating Sentences. On a separate piece of paper, write a paragraph about the picture below. Use some of the following long *i* words in your sentences.

hire	life	line	fine
time	lifetime	knife	like
overtime	pride	nice	beside
retire	invite	smile	excitement

9 Writing Sentences. On the lines below, write the sentences that you hear.

1. _____

2. _____

3. _____

4. _____

5. _____

6. _____

7. _____

8. _____

Lesson 17

The Word Families *ise*, *ize*, and *y*

Sight Words			
liquid	weigh	ounce	oz.
fluid	weight	pound	lb.

Word Families

ise

1 Listening

Listen to the sound *ise* makes in these words.

rise	wise	surprise	despise
arise	advise	supervise	disguise
	revise	advertise	exercise

ize

Listen to the sound *ize* makes in these words.

size	realize	memorize	recognize
prize	criticize	alphabetize	

y

Listen to the sound *y* makes in these words.

cry	fry	deny	apply
dry	shy	rely	supply
try	why	reply	identify

2 Writing Words. On the lines below, write the words that you hear.

1. _____   5. _____   9. _____

2. _____   6. _____   10. _____

3. _____   7. _____   11. _____

4. _____   8. _____   12. _____

3 **Using Sight Words.** Fill in the blanks in the sentences below with the sight words from this lesson. Use your dictionary if necessary.

1. (ounces, pound) There are 16 _____ in a _____.

2. (fluid, liquid) A _____ flows easily. A _____ is wet.

3. (weigh, weight) To find the _____ of something you must _____ it.

4 **Dictionary Skills: Abbreviations.** Match the abbreviations below with the measurements they represent. Use your dictionary if you need to.

gal.   hr   lb.   mph   pt.
gm   kg   min   oz.   qt.

1. ounce _____   6. gram _____

2. pound _____   7. kilogram _____

3. minute _____   8. pint _____

4. hour _____   9. quart _____

5. miles per hour _____   10. gallon _____

5 **Adding Endings to Words That End in Cy.** When adding an ending to a word that ends in **Cy**, change the *y* to *i* unless the ending begins with *i*. Do not add *-s* to words that end in **Cy**. Instead, change the *y* to *i* and add *-es*. Add the endings above the columns to each word below. The first one has been done to get you started.

	-es	*-ed*	*-ing*
1. cry	cries	cried	crying
2. try	_____	_____	_____
3. dry	_____	_____	_____
4. deny	_____	_____	_____
5. reply	_____	_____	_____
6. supply	_____	_____	_____

6 Review of Adding Endings. Add the endings above the columns to each word below.

	-s or -es	-ed	-ing
1. revise			
2. apply			
3. inquire			
4. identify			
5. smile			
6. sacrifice			
7. rely			
8. advertise			

7 Word Building. Words from the *ise* family are usually pronounced like the *ize* family words. Fill in the missing letters in the sentences below with either *ise* or *ize*. Use your dictionary to help you select the correct spelling if necessary.

1. Mike paid us a surpr__ __ __ visit last week.

2. Eileen had changed so much we hardly recogn__ __ __d her.

3. It is important to get plenty of good exerc__ __ __.

4. I real__ __ __ that you are busy, but we really need your help.

5. What would you adv__ __ __ me to do about this problem?

6. Gail apolog__ __ __d for not being able to come to the meeting.

7. Tonight I have to memor__ __ __ my lines for the play.

8. Mr. Rice is going to superv__ __ __ the Wednesday night craft class.

8 **The Word Families *ice* and *ise*.** Write each word your teacher dictates in the correct column below.

ice	*ise*
1. _____	1. _____
2. _____	2. _____
3. _____	3. _____
4. _____	4. _____
5. _____	5. _____

Words in the *ise* family are usually pronounced /īz/. If you hear /īs/, it is probably spelled *ice*.

9 **Writing Sentences.** On the lines below, write the sentences that you hear.

1. _____

2. _____

3. _____

4. _____

5. _____

6. _____

7. _____

8. _____

9. _____

10. _____

_____

Lesson 18

The Word Families *ight*, *igh*, *ign*, *ind*, and *ild*

Sight Words			
altogether	usual	door	style
terrible	straight	floor	type

Word Families

1 Listening

ight

Listen to the sound *ight* makes in these words.

might	fight	night	light
sight	right	tonight	delight
tight	bright	midnight	flashlight

igh

Listen to the sound *igh* makes in these words.

high	highway	sigh	thigh

ign

Listen to the sound *ign* makes in these words.

sign	design	align
assign	resign	benign

ind

Listen to the sound *ind* makes in these words.

bind	mind	kind	blind
find	remind	kindness	behind

ild

Listen to the sound *ild* makes in these words.

child	grandchild	mild	wild

2 Writing Words. On the lines below, write the words that you hear.

1. _____   4. _____   7. _____

2. _____   5. _____   8. _____

3. _____   6. _____   9. _____

Word Building. Add one of the suffixes below to each word to make another form of the word.

-ed   -ing   -ish   -ly   -ness   -y

1. might _____   6. blind _____

2. remind _____   7. child _____

3. mild _____   8. kind _____

4. sigh _____   9. bright _____

5. tight _____   10. fight _____

 Word Building with *ign* Words. Add the prefixes and suffixes to the *ign* words below. Then use two of the words you formed in sentences and write the sentences on the lines at the bottom of the page. Look up their meanings in the dictionary if necessary.

1. align + ed _____

2. re + align _____

3. align + ment _____

4. re + align + ment _____

5. assign + ed _____

6. un + assign + ed _____

7. assign + ment _____

8. re + assign + ment _____

1. _____

_____

2. _____

_____

5 **Patterns for Spelling Long *i*.** Write the words that your teacher dictates.

1. _____   3. _____   5. _____

2. _____   4. _____

Five different patterns that produce a long *i* sound are used in the words above. Now write one other word for each long *i* spelling pattern.

1. iCe _____   4. ign _____

2. y _____   5. iCd _____

3. igh _____

6 **Dictionary Skills: Finding the Correct Spelling.** Because there are a number of ways to spell long *i*, sometimes you won't remember which one to use. If you can't remember which spelling of long *i* to use, or if the word is new to you, check your dictionary.

Find the correct spelling of the words spelled phonetically below based on the meanings given. Write the words on the lines provided.

Phonetic Spelling	Meaning	Correct Spelling
1. /săt´ĭs fī/	to fulfill a desire or need	_____
2. /rĕ vīz´/	to change or improve	_____
3. /blīnd´fōld/	a cover for the eyes	_____
4. /mă līn´/	to say something harmful; to slander	_____
5. /mĕm´ə rīz/	to learn by heart	_____
6. /blīt/	a disease that destroys plants	_____
7. /dī´nə mīt´/	an explosive used for blasting	_____
8. /pīp´līn´/	a row of tubes for carrying fluids	_____

7 **Writing Words by Syllables.** Write the words your teacher dictates by syllables. Then write the entire word. Use the syllable types to help you spell the word.

First Syllable	Second Syllable	Third Syllable		Whole Word
1. _____	_____			_____
2. _____	_____			_____
3. _____	_____			_____
4. _____	_____			_____
5. _____	_____	_____		_____
6. _____	_____	_____		_____

8 **Hearing Differences.** Many words sound almost like other words. If they are not carefully spoken or heard, they may be misspelled. Listen carefully to the pairs of words you hear. Then write the endings in the blanks at the ends of the words.

1. mi_____   mi_____   3. wi_____   wi_____

2. fi_____   fi_____   4. mi_____   mi_____

9 **Writing Sentences.** On the lines below, write the sentences that you hear.

1. _____
2. _____
3. _____
4. _____
5. _____
6. _____
7. _____
8. _____

Review of Unit 3

The Long *i*

1 **Word Building with iCe Families.** Add one of the word families listed below to each of the consonants or blends to make a word.

ime	*ike*	*ipe*	*ine*	*ide*	*ife*	*ise*
ibe	*ice*	*ile*	*ire*	*ite*	*ive*	*ize*

1. b_____
2. d_____
3. h_____
4. l_____

5. m_____
6. p_____
7. s_____
8. w_____

9. br_____
10. pr_____
11. tw_____
12. wh_____

2 **Other Patterns for Spelling Long *i*.** One pattern that produces long *i* is iCe. Four other patterns that you learned in Unit 3 are listed below. Write three words for each pattern.

1. igh _____ _____ _____
2. ign _____ _____ _____
3. y _____ _____ _____
4. iCd _____ _____ _____

3 **Familiar Sayings.** Fill in the blanks in these familiar sayings with the long *i* words below.

bride	eyes	kite	shines	time
divided	fly	nine	sight	united

1. Go _____ a _____.

2. A stitch in _____ saves _____.

3. Happy is the _____ that the sun _____ on.

4. _____ we stand, _____ we fall.

5. You are a _____ for sore _____.

4 **Reviewing Patterns for Endings.** Review these six patterns for adding endings.

1. **Regular Endings.** Add the ending without changing anything in the root word or the ending.

2. **Doubling Pattern 1.** Double the final consonant if the word has one syllable, one vowel, and one final consonant, and the ending begins with a vowel. Do not double *w* or *x*.

3. **Silent *e* Pattern 1.** Drop the final silent *e* if the ending begins with a vowel.

4. **The Ending -es.** When a word ends in *s, x, z, ch*, or *sh*, add *-es* instead of *-s*.

5. **Changing *y* to *i*.** When adding an ending to a word that ends in C*y*, change the *y* to *i* unless the ending begins with *i*. Add *-es* instead of *-s*.

6. **Changing *f* to *v*.** The plural of some words which end in *f* or *fe* is formed by changing the *f* or *fe* to *v* and adding *-es*.

Write the root word for each of the words listed below. Then write the number of the pattern which was followed when the ending was added. The first one has been done to get you started.

	Root Word	Pattern
1. singer	sing	1
2. sadder		
3. leashes		
4. wives		
5. smiling		
6. shelves		
7. stylish		
8. skies		
9. ripped		
10. tried		

5 **Adding Endings.** Add the designated endings to each of the words below.

1. rely + ing   _____

2. dine + er   _____

3. life + s *or* es _____

4. big + er   _____

5. bike + ing   _____

6. fix + s *or* es   _____

7. sew + ing   _____

8. deny + al   _____

9. reply + s *or* es _____

10. speech + s *or* es _____

11. light + ly   _____

12. tap + ed   _____

13. greedy + er   _____

14. try + al   _____

15. kidney + s *or* es _____

16. beach + s *or* es _____

17. rid + ing   _____

18. ride + ing   _____

19. leaf + s *or* es _____

20. invite + ed   _____

6 **Reviewing Syllable Types**

1. Circle each closed syllable below.

con   bin   o   vite   fun   bo   tle   bock   teem   ip

2. Circle each open syllable below.

bo   in   o   vite   be   tle   cape   la   tain   ra

3. Circle each Cle syllable below.

bo   in   o   vite   tle   hap   il   ble   re   i

4. Circle each VCe syllable below.

cate   in   o   vite   tle   hap   il   cape   ceal   re

5. Circle each double vowel syllable below.

cate   in   ceed   vite   tle   beat   tain   ble   ceal   hap

Writing Words by Syllables. Write the words your teacher dictates by syllables. Then write the entire word on the line provided.

First Syllable	Second Syllable	Third Syllable	Fourth Syllable		Whole Word
1. _____	_____	_____			_____
2. _____	_____	_____			_____
3. _____	_____	_____			_____
4. _____	_____	_____	_____		_____
5. _____	_____	_____	_____		_____
6. _____	_____	_____	_____		_____

Challenge word:

_____ _____ _____ _____ _____ _____

8 **Using Irregular Verbs.** Fill in the blanks in the sentences below with the correct form of the verb in parentheses. Look up the verbs in your dictionary if necessary.

1. (find) Have you _____ your notebook yet?

2. (slide) The batter _____ into second base and was safe.

3. (ride) Have you ever _____ on a trolley?

4. (rise) I was awake before the sun _____ this morning.

5. (fight) The committee has _____ hard to get the plans accepted.

6. (bind) Dwight has _____ the crates with good, strong rope.

7. (write) I have _____ them several letters, but they haven't responded.

8. (rise) The number of graduates has _____ sharply over the past five years.

9 **Creating Sentences.** On a separate sheet of paper, write a story about the three pictures below. Use some of the following long *i* words from Unit 3.

night	fright	shine	recognize	reply
time	while	flashlight	sight	criticize
tired	try	surprise	why	apologize
wife	excited	identify	remind	sacrifice

2 a.m.

Moments later

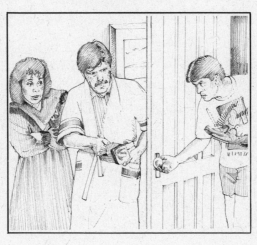

Still later

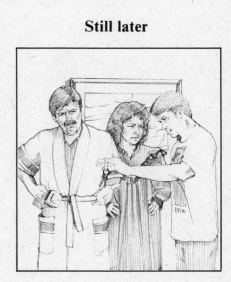

10 **Writing Sentences.** On the lines below, write the sentences that you hear.

1. _____

2. _____

3. _____

4. _____

5. _____

6. _____

7. _____

8. _____

11 **Crossword Puzzle.** Use the clues below to complete the puzzle. Most of the answers are word family and sight words from Unit 3.

Across

1. Get up
3. Measured the weight of something
6. This connects your arm to your body.
10. When two words end in the same sound they do this.
11. The opposite of answer
13. May: I ____ go shopping tonight.
14. Gentle: A ____ breeze blew.
16. To operate a car
17. The person who steers the car
18. Made up your mind: Have you ____ to go with us?

Down

1. Reply
2. A long, drawn-out breath
3. The opposite of tame
4. ____ and seek
5. A plan or pattern used for making something
6. Where the clouds are
7. Beyond the regular hours
8. Not a solid or gas; something wet
9. What you do to stay fit
12. What the clock tells
13. You use this to think.
15. Changed the color: She ____ her rug blue.

Lesson 19

The Word Families *ope*, *one*, *oke*, *ome*, and *ove*

Sight Words		
most	ready	always
almost	already	all right

Word Families

1 Listening

ope

Listen to the sound *ope* makes in these words.

hope	rope	envelope
cope	slope	telescope

one

Listen to the sound *one* makes in these words.

bone	phone	lone	shone
tone	telephone	alone	stone
zone	postpone	lonely	

oke

Listen to the sound *oke* makes in these words.

joke	smoke	broke	revoke
poke	spoke	broken	provoke
woke	stroke		

ome

Listen to the sound *ome* makes in these words.

dome	homeless	Nome
home	homesick	Rome

ove

Listen to the sound *ove* makes in these words.

cove	rove	grove	stove
drove	wove	strove	stovepipe

2 Writing Words. On the lines below, write the words that you hear.

1. _____   4. _____   7. _____

2. _____   5. _____   8. _____

3. _____   6. _____   9. _____

3 Word Building. Add either *ope*, *one*, *oke*, *ome*, or *ove* to each of the consonants to make a word. Do not make the same word twice.

1. c_____   4. j_____   7. dr_____

2. h_____   5. r_____   8. gr_____

3. h_____   6. t_____   9. st_____

4 Using Sight Words. Fill in the blanks in the sentences below with the sight words from this lesson. Use each word only once.

1. A square _____ has four sides of equal length.

2. The Earth is _____ a perfect sphere.

3. China is the _____ populous country on Earth.

4. Firemen must be _____ to respond at a moment's notice.

5. Many scientists believe the greenhouse effect has _____ begun.

6. It is _____ to plant seedlings when there is no more danger of frost.

5 The VCe Syllable Type. As you know, a **VC**e syllable ends in a silent *e*. This silent *e* usually causes the vowel to be long. For each of the vowels below, write three words that follow the **VC**e pattern and contain the long vowel sound.

1. a _____   _____   _____

2. e _____   _____   _____

3. i _____   _____   _____

4. o _____   _____   _____

6 **Review of Silent *e* Pattern 1.** The silent *e* at the end of a word is dropped when an ending starting with a vowel is added. The silent *e* is not dropped when the ending starts with a consonant. Add the endings to the words below and write the new words on the lines provided.

1. cope + ed _____

2. zone + ing _____

3. hope + ful _____

4. joke + er _____

5. dome + ed _____

6. spoke + en _____

7. smoke + er _____

8. phone + ing _____

9. bone + less _____

10. broke + er _____

7 **Reviewing Syllable Types.** Write each syllable below on a line under the correct heading.

reel	gle	so	muf	kle
gal	ment	re	e	voke
tail	ade	tle	nate	aim
pro	tract	file	cle	veal

Closed

1. _____

2. _____

3. _____

4. _____

Open

1. _____

2. _____

3. _____

4. _____

Cle

1. _____

2. _____

3. _____

4. _____

VCe

1. _____

2. _____

3. _____

4. _____

Double

1. _____

2. _____

3. _____

4. _____

8 **Writing Words by Syllables.** Write the words that you hear one syllable at a time. Then write the whole word on the line at the right. Use the syllable types to help you spell the word.

First Syllable	Second Syllable	Third Syllable		Whole Word
1. _____	_____			_____
2. _____	_____			_____
3. _____	_____			_____
4. _____	_____	_____		_____
5. _____	_____	_____		_____
6. _____	_____	_____		_____
7. _____	_____	_____		_____
8. _____	_____	_____		_____

9 **Writing Sentences.** On the lines below, write the sentences that you hear.

1. _____

2. _____

3. _____

4. _____

5. _____

6. _____

7. _____
_____

8. _____
_____

Lesson 20

The Word Families *obe*, *ote*, *ode*, *ore*, *ose*, and *oze*

Sight Words		
woman	hurry	spouse
women	worry	husband

Word Families

1 Listening

obe

Listen to the sound *obe* makes in these words.

robe	lobe	strobe
probe	globe	

ote

Listen to the sound *ote* makes in these words.

note	vote	quote	devote
notebook	voter	wrote	remote

ode

Listen to the sound *ode* makes in these words.

code	mode	erode
zip code	rode	explode

ore

Listen to the sound *ore* makes in these words.

ore	tore	chore	before
core	store	shore	folklore
sore	restore	shoreline	moreover

ose

Listen to the sound *ose* makes in these words.

hose	pose	close	chose
nose	expose	disclose	those
rose	suppose		

oze

Listen to the sound *oze* makes in these words.

doze	bulldozer	froze	frozen

2 Writing Words. On the lines below, write the words that you hear.

1. _____   5. _____   9. _____

2. _____   6. _____   10. _____

3. _____   7. _____   11. _____

4. _____   8. _____   12. _____

3 Word Building. Many words from the *ose* family are pronounced like the *oze* family words. Fill in the missing letters in the sentences below with either *ose* or *oze*.

1. We left the h__ __ __ outside and it fr__ __ __.

2. R__ __ __ wanted to stay awake for the late show, but she d__ __ __d off.

3. I supp__ __ __ you ch__ __ __ that tie to go with your shirt.

4. Th__ __ __ flowers were exp__ __ __d to the cold and were fr__ __ __n.

5. Mike drove the bulld__ __ __r right through the r__ __ __ bushes.

4 Finding Root Words. Write the root word for each of the words below on the lines provided.

1. hopeful   _____   8. lonely   _____

2. denote   _____   9. rewrote   _____

3. compose   _____   10. disclose _____

4. telephone _____   11. remotely _____

5. homeless   _____   12. telescope _____

6. exposure   _____   13. notable   _____

7. voter   _____   14. global   _____

5 **Adding Endings.** Add the endings to each of the words below and write the new words on the lines provided.

1. joke + ing   _____

2. robe + ed   _____

3. rob + ed   _____

4. store + age   _____

5. quote + able   _____

6. snore + ed   _____

7. globe + al   _____

8. hope + ing   _____

9. hop + ing   _____

10. erode + ing   _____

11. remote + ly   _____

12. jersey + s *or* es   _____

13. probe + ing   _____

14. deny + s *or* es   _____

15. teach + s *or* es   _____

16. disclose + ed   _____

17. wolf + s *or* es   _____

18. lone + ly + ness   _____

19. suppose + ed + ly   _____

20. hope + less + ly   _____

6 **Creating Sentences.** Choose five of the words you wrote in Exercise 5 and use them in sentences.

1. _____

_____

2. _____

_____

3. _____

_____

4. _____

_____

5. _____

_____

7 **Using Words.** Fill in the blanks in the story with the words listed below. Use each word only once.

arose	exposed	spoke	voters
bulldozer	hurry	those	worried
chose	ignored	voted	wrote

Many people _____ in the local elections last week. They _____ a new mayor and three new members of the town council.

Eight months ago, a problem _____. Toxic waste was _____ when a _____ uncovered an old dump site. This _____ many people. They wanted the toxic waste cleaned up in a _____. Many people _____ letters to the editor of the newspaper and _____ out at town council meetings.

But the mayor and several councilors _____ their demands. Last week, the _____ turned _____ officials out of office when they went to the polls.

8 **Writing Sentences.** On the lines below, write the sentences that you hear.

1. _____
2. _____
3. _____
4. _____
5. _____
6. _____
7. _____
8. _____

Lesson 21

The Word Families *ole*, *oll*, *old*, and *olt*

Sight Words			
during	moth	canoe	soul
skiing	cloth	promise	spirit

Word Families

1 **Listening**

ole

Listen to the sound *ole* makes in these words.

mole	sole	whole	hole
pole	stole	wholesome	keyhole
role	parole	wholesale	buttonhole

oll

Listen to the sound *oll* makes in these words.

roll	poll	stroll	knoll
enroll	toll	swollen	wholly

old

Listen to the sound *old* makes in these words.

hold	bold	golden
sold	cold	withhold
told	scold	blindfold

olt

Listen to the sound *olt* makes in these words.

colt	bolt	revolt
jolted	voltage	

2 **Writing Words.** On the lines below, write the words that you hear.

1. _____   5. _____   9. _____

2. _____   6. _____   10. _____

3. _____   7. _____   11. _____

4. _____   8. _____   12. _____

3 **Dictionary Skills: Finding the Correct Spelling.** There are two common spellings for /ōl/: *oll* and *ole*. Use the dictionary to find the correct spelling for the words below based on the meanings given. When you find the spelling that matches the meaning, write the word in the appropriate column.

Phonetic Spelling	Meaning	oll	ole
1. /bōl/	a seedpod of the cotton plant	_____	_____
2. /dōl/	to give out small portions	_____	_____
3. /drōl/	amusing, comical	_____	_____
4. /tăd′pōl/	a young frog or toad	_____	_____
5. /skrōl/	a roll of writing material	_____	_____
6. /loop′hōl/	a way to avoid or evade something	_____	_____

4 **Dictionary Skills: Homonyms.** Answer the following questions using your dictionary if necessary.

1. Does a doughnut have a *hole* or a *whole*? _____

2. Was the flag on top of the *pole* or the *poll*? _____

3. Did the car *role* or *roll* down the hill? _____

4. Is the spirit of something a *sole* or a *soul*? _____

5 **Word Building.** Words in the *old* family sound like the past tense of words in the *oll* and *ole* families. Fill in the blanks in the sentences below with *old*, *oled*, or *olled*. Use your dictionary to check any spellings you are not sure of.

1. Are you enr_____ in any courses this semester?

2. That bread has m_____ on it.

3. Dora str_____ along the deserted beach.

4. I asked Norman to f_____ his clothes neatly.

5. When Ryan broke his leg, we cons_____ him with a gallon of ice cream.

6 **Dictionary Skills: Irregular Verbs.** Look up the following verbs in the dictionary, and write the different forms in the appropriate columns.

Present Tense	Past Tense	Have, Has, or Had + Verb	-ing Form of Verb
1. sell			
2. speak			
3. hold			
4. choose			
5. tell			
6. break			
7. swell			
8. freeze			
9. shine			
10. wear			

7 **Syllable Types.** The five types of syllables you have studied so far are listed below. An example of each type is given. Write another example of each type of syllable on the lines provided.

Syllable Type	Example	Your Example
1. Closed	hot	
2. Open	so	
3. Cle	ple	
4. VCe	ope	
5. Double Vowel	oat	

8 **Writing Words by Syllables.** Write the words your teacher dictates by syllables. Then write the entire word on the line provided.

	First Syllable	Second Syllable	Third Syllable	Fourth Syllable	Whole Word
1.	_____	_____	_____		_____
2.	_____	_____	_____		_____
3.	_____	_____	_____		_____
4.	_____	_____	_____		_____
5.	_____	_____	_____		_____
6.	_____	_____	_____	_____	_____
7.	_____	_____	_____	_____	_____
8.	_____	_____	_____	_____	_____

Challenge word:

_____ _____ _____ _____ _____ _____

9 **Writing Sentences.** On the lines below, write the sentences that you hear.

1. _____

2. _____

3. _____

4. _____

5. _____

6. _____

7. _____

8. _____

Lesson 22

The Word Families *oat*, *oam*, *oal*, *oad*, *oan*, *oak*, *oast*, and *oach*

Word Families

1 Listening

oat

Listen to the sound *oat* makes in these words.

oats	coat	boat	gloat
float	overcoat	sailboat	throat

oam

Listen to the sound *oam* makes in these words.

foam	roam	styrofoam

oal

Listen to the sound *oal* makes in these words.

coal	charcoal	goal	field goal

oad

Listen to the sound *oad* makes in these words.

load	road	goad
carload	railroad	toad

oan

Listen to the sound *oan* makes in these words.

Joan	loan	moan	groan

oak

Listen to the sound *oak* makes in these words.

oak	cloak	croak	soak

oast

Listen to the sound *oast* makes in these words.

boast	roast	coastal	coaster
coast	toast	coastline	roller coaster

oach

Listen to the sound *oach* makes in these words.

coach	stagecoach	cockroach	poached

2 **Writing Words.** On the lines below, write the words that you hear.

1. _____   5. _____   9. _____

2. _____   6. _____   10. _____

3. _____   7. _____   11. _____

4. _____   8. _____   12. _____

3 **Using Sight Words.** Fill in the blanks in the sentences below with the sight words from this lesson. Use each word only once. Your dictionary will help if you need to check the facts.

1. There are 12 inches in a _____ and 36 inches in a _____.

2. There are one hundred _____ in a meter.

3. A _____ is a little over 39 inches long.

4. There are one thousand meters in a _____.

5. There are about two and one-half centimeters in an _____.

Arrange the sight words in order from the smallest measure to the largest and write them on the lines below. The first one is done to get you started.

centimeter, _____

_____

4 **Finding a Pattern.** In each pair of words, underline the word that has a long vowel sound.

1. cot — coat   2. road — rod   3. got — goat

What letter has been added to the underlined words to make the *o* long? _____

Where has the letter been added? _____

Can you hear the added letter in the underlined words? _____

What sound does *oa* make in the words above? _____

Pattern: The letters *oa* usually make the sound of long *o*.

5 **Dictionary Skills: Abbreviations.** Write the abbreviation for each sight word on the lines provided. Use your dictionary if necessary.

1. centimeter _____

2. foot _____

3. inch _____

4. kilometer _____

5. meter _____

6. yard _____

6 **Dictionary Skills: Homonyms**

Part A. Answer the following questions, using a dictionary when you need to.

1. Is a car driven on a *road* or a *rode*? _____

2. Would you go to a bank for a *loan* or a *lone*? _____

3. Is a vein of gold ore a *load* or a *lode*? _____

4. Is *Roam* or *Rome* the capital of Italy? _____

Part B. Fill in each blank in the sentences below with the correct spelling of the phonetically spelled words.

1. /rōd/   Joe _____ on the Long Island Rail_____.

2. /lōd/   The miners took a _____ of silver from the mother _____.

3. /rōm/   Cory _____ed around Europe and ended up in _____.

4. /lōn/   Joan was the _____ applicant to get a _____.

7 **Hearing Differences.** Careless speaking and listening can result in poor spelling. Many words sound almost like other words. Listen carefully to the sets of words you hear. Then write the endings on the lines provided.

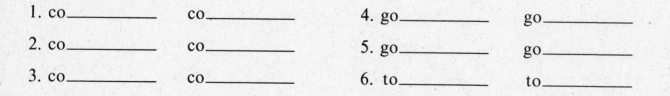

1. co_____   co_____   4. go_____   go_____

2. co_____   co_____   5. go_____   go_____

3. co_____   co_____   6. to_____   to_____

8 **Creating Sentences.** Four different means of transportation are pictured below. Imagine that you have taken a trip using one of these methods of travel. On a separate sheet of paper, write a story describing your trip. Use some of the following long *o* words in your story.

stagecoach	road	coat	hope
boat	roam	load	before
railroad	rode	whole	postpone
carload	drove	alone	homesick

9 **Writing Sentences.** On the lines below, write the sentences that you hear.

1. _____

2. _____

3. _____

4. _____

5. _____

6. _____

7. _____

8. _____

Lesson 23

The Word Families *o*, *oe*, *ow*, and *own*

```
┌─────────────────────────────────┐
│            Sight Words          │
│      how    town    howl        │
│      now    clown   towel       │
└─────────────────────────────────┘
```

Word Families

1 Listening

o

Listen to the sound *o* makes in these words.

omit	go	so	local
over	ago	sofa	locate
obey	piano	solo	donate
ocean	radio	Soviet	program

oe

Listen to the sound *oe* makes in these words.

doe	foe	toe
hoe	woe	tiptoe
Joe	goes	oboe

ow

Listen to the sound *ow* makes in these words.

low	row	tow	narrow
blow	crow	know	shadow
below	grow	show	window
slowly	throw	snowflake	rainbow
overflow	borrow	elbow	tomorrow

own

Listen to the sound *own* makes in these words.

own	blown	known	grown
ownership	flown	shown	thrown

2 **Writing Words.** On the lines below, write the words that you hear.

1. _____   5. _____   9. _____

2. _____   6. _____   10. _____

3. _____   7. _____   11. _____

4. _____   8. _____   12. _____

3 **Dictionary Skills: Homonyms.** Answer the following questions using a dictionary if necessary.

1. Is a female deer a *doe* or a *dough*?   _____

2. If something has gotten bigger, has it *groan* or *grown*?   _____

3. Does a king sit on a *throne* or a *thrown*?   _____

4. When you plant seeds, do you *so* them or *sow* them?   _____

5. Do you *no* or *know* how to do something?   _____

6. Has the movie been *shone* or *shown* many times?   _____

4 **Adding Endings to Words That End in *o* or *oe*.** Generally, when endings are added to words that end in *o*, no letters are added, dropped, or changed.

     Examples: radio + ed = radioed   solo + ist = soloist

When endings are added to words that end in *oe*, the silent *e* is dropped if the ending begins with any vowel except *i* or *y*.

     Examples: hoe + ed = hoed   tiptoe + ing = tiptoeing

Add the endings to the words below.

1. echo + ing   _____   5. veto + ing   _____

2. hero + ic   _____   6. woe + ful + ly   _____

3. Joe + y   _____   7. canoe + ing   _____

4. canoe + ed   _____   8. toe + hold   _____

5 **Plurals of Words Ending with *o*.** Some words that end in *o* have -*s* added to form the plural. Others have -*es* added. For some words, either -*s* or -*es* can be added. Look up the following words in the dictionary and write their plural forms in the appropriate columns.

	Add -*s*	**Add -*es***
1. video	_____	_____
2. ratio	_____	_____
3. patio	_____	_____
4. stereo	_____	_____
5. radio	_____	_____
6. trio	_____	_____
7. echo	_____	_____
8. veto	_____	_____
9. hero	_____	_____
10. tomato	_____	_____
11. potato	_____	_____
12. piano	_____	_____
13. solo	_____	_____
14. alto	_____	_____
15. soprano	_____	_____
16. zero	_____	_____
17. tornado	_____	_____
18. volcano	_____	_____

6 **Finding Patterns.** Fill in the blanks below to discover two patterns which will help you to know whether to add *-s* or *-es* to form the plural of words ending in *o*.

Part A. Write the plurals of the words from Exercise 5 that end with two vowels.

1. _____   3. _____   5. _____

2. _____   4. _____   6. _____

    Pattern: Add _____ to form the plural of words that end with **Vo**.

Part B. Write the plurals of words in the field of music (*piano, solo, alto* and *soprano*).

_____   _____   _____   _____

    Pattern: Add _____ to form the plural of words ending with *o* from the field of music.

Part C. Following the patterns above, write the plural of these words:

1. curio   _____   4. banjo   _____

2. rodeo   _____   5. piccolo _____

3. studio   _____   6. cello   _____

7 **Writing Sentences.** On the lines below, write the sentences that you hear.

1. _____

2. _____

3. _____

4. _____

5. _____

6. _____

7. _____

8. _____

Review of Unit 4

The Long *o*

1 **Word Building with oCe Families.** Add one of the word families listed below to each of the consonants to make a word. Do not make the same word twice.

ope	*ome*	*ote*	*ose*
one	*ove*	*ode*	*oze*
oke	*obe*	*ore*	*ole*

1. c_____
2. h_____
3. j_____
4. l_____
5. m_____
6. n_____
7. n_____

8. p_____
9. r_____
10. r_____
11. t_____
12. v_____
13. w_____
14. z_____

15. cl_____
16. fr_____
17. gr_____
18. sp_____
19. st_____
20. st_____
21. wh_____

2 **Other Patterns for Spelling Long *o*.** One pattern that produces long *o* is oCe. Six other patterns which you learned in Unit 4 are listed below. Write three words for each pattern.

1. olC _____ _____ _____
2. oaC _____ _____ _____
3. o _____ _____ _____
4. oe _____ _____ _____
5. ow _____ _____ _____
6. own _____ _____ _____

3 **Dictionary Skills: Irregular Verbs.** Write the forms of the verbs below in the appropriate columns. Use your dictionary if necessary.

Present Tense	Past Tense	Have, Has, or Had + Verb	-ing Form of Verb
1. go	_____	_____	_____
2. fly	_____	_____	_____
3. blow	_____	_____	_____
4. grow	_____	_____	_____
5. know	_____	_____	_____

4 **Using Irregular Verbs.** Fill in the sentences below with the correct form of the verb in parentheses.

1. (sell) Rose _____ her old sofa at the garage sale.

2. (tell) Doreen _____ me she couldn't baby-sit today.

3. (hold) Joe _____ on to the tow rope after he fell into the water.

4. (break) Tony _____ Owen's record in the high jump yesterday.

5. (speak) Have you _____ to Norman about going to the movies with us?

6. (choose) I wanted cheesecake for dessert, but Cory _____ apple pie.

7. (freeze) Grove's Pond was _____ for four months last winter.

8. (wear) The neighborhood kids have _____ a path across our yard.

9. (tear) Joan _____ up the letter and threw it away.

10. (throw) All of the magazines that you saved got _____ out by mistake.

5 **Writing Words.** On the lines below, write the words that you hear.

1. _____	4. _____	7. _____
2. _____	5. _____	8. _____
3. _____	6. _____	9. _____

6 **Writing Words by Syllables.** Write the words your teacher dictates by syllables. Then write the entire word on the line provided.

First Syllable	Second Syllable	Third Syllable	Fourth Syllable	Whole Word
1. _____	_____			_____
2. _____	_____	_____		_____
3. _____	_____	_____		_____
4. _____	_____	_____		_____
5. _____	_____	_____		_____
6. _____	_____	_____		_____
7. _____	_____	_____		_____
8. _____	_____	_____		_____

7 **Writing Sentences.** On the lines below, write the sentences that you hear.

1. _____

2. _____

3. _____

4. _____

5. _____

6. _____

7. _____

8. _____

9. _____

10. _____

_____

8 **Crossword Puzzle.** Use the clues below to complete the puzzle. Most of the answers are word family or sight words from Unit 4.

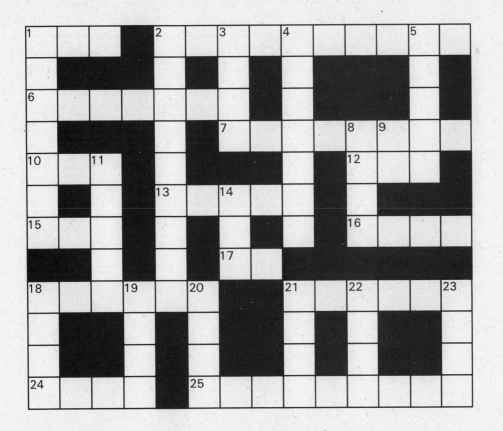

Across

1. A tool used by farmers and gardeners
2. You can call long distance on these.
6. Filled with fluid: His sprained ankle is _____.
7. A letter is mailed in this.
10. What we breathe
12. A homonym for or
13. A flowing garment used as a coat
15. Past tense of do
16. To nap; to sleep lightly
17. The opposite of yes
18. People cook on these.
21. A passage inside the neck
24. Past tense of weave
25. Healthy, nourishing

Down

1. A male spouse
2. This is used to see stars.
3. The only one
4. To irritate or make angry
5. To run off and get married
8. Something carried; a burden
9. Indicates a choice: either this _____ that
11. An instrument used to receive broadcasts
14. Possess: Do you _____ your home?
18. To explain or display: _____ and tell
19. To go to the polls to elect someone
20. What rain becomes in winter
21. A charge for using a bridge or highway
22. Uses oars to move the boat
23. A sound having a certain quality: a pleasant _____ of voice

Review of Book 2

The Long Vowel Word Families

Syllable Type	Long a Lessons 1-6	Long e Lessons 7-14		Long i Lessons 15-18	Long o Lessons 19-23
VCe				ibe	obe
	ace			ice	
	ade			ide	ode
	afe			ife	
	age				
	ake			ike	oke
	ale			ile	ole
	ame			ime	ome
	ane			ine	one
	ape			ipe	ope
	are			ire	ore
	ase			ise	ose
	ate			ite	ote
	ave			ive	ove
	aze			ize	oze
VVC		eech	each		oach
or	aid	eed	ead		oad
VVCC		eek	eak		oak
	ail	eel	eal		oal
	aim	eem	eam		oam
	ain	een	ean		oan
	aint				
		eep	eap		
	air	eer	ear		
			east		oast
	ait	eet	eat		oat
V	ay	e		y	o
or		ea			oe
VV		ee			
		ey			
		y			
Other Syllables	aise	ease		igh	old
	ange	eeze		ight	oll
	aste	eave		ign	olt
	ary	ceive		ild	ow
	azy	ly		ind	own

1 Patterns for Spelling Long Vowels. Several ways to spell each of the long vowels are represented on the chart. Write one word that uses each of the spellings given below.

Long a

1. aCe _____   3. ay _____   5. ange _____

2. aiC _____   4. aCy _____   6. aste _____

Long e

1. e _____   4. eaC _____   7. eCe _____

2. ee _____   5. ea _____   8. y _____

3. eeC _____   6. ey _____   9. ly _____

Long i

1. iCe _____   3. ign _____   5. iCd _____

2. igh _____   4. y _____   6. ight _____

Long o

1. oCe _____   3. olC _____   5. oe _____

2. oaC _____   4. o _____   6. ow _____

2 Writing Words. On the lines below, write the words that you hear.

1. _____   7. _____   13. _____

2. _____   8. _____   14. _____

3. _____   9. _____   15. _____

4. _____   10. _____   16. _____

5. _____   11. _____   17. _____

6. _____   12. _____   18. _____

3 **Reviewing Patterns for Endings.** Fill in the blanks below to review the patterns you have learned for adding endings.

1. **Doubling Pattern 1.** Double the final consonant if a word has one _____, one _____, and one _____ consonant, and the ending begins with a _____. Do not double _____ or *x*.

2. **Silent *e* Pattern 1.** Drop a silent *e* at the end of a word if the ending begins with a _____.

3. **The Ending -*es*.** When a word ends in *s*, _____, *z*, _____, or _____, add -*es* instead of -*s* to form the plural.

4. **Changing *y* to *i*.** When a word ends in C*y*, change the *y* to *i* before adding any ending that doesn't begin with _____. Add _____ instead of -*s* to form the plural.

5. **Changing *f* to *v*.** To form the plural of some words that end in *f* or *fe*, change the *f* or *fe* to _____ and add _____.

6. **Words That End in *o* and *oe*.** Words that end in _____ are not changed when endings are added. Some words that end in *o* have -*s* added to form the plural, while others have _____ added. Words that end in *oe* drop the silent *e* if an ending begins with any _____ except *i* or *y*.

4 **Adding Endings.** Add the endings to the words below.

1. hurry + ing _____
2. quote + able _____
3. tow + ed _____
4. delay + ed _____
5. radio + s *or* es _____
6. hop + ing _____
7. hope + ing _____
8. beach + s *or* es _____
9. journey + s *or* es _____
10. worry + ed _____
11. desire + able _____
12. hoe + ing _____
13. knife + s *or* es _____
14. like + ly + est _____

5 **Review of Syllable Types.** Write one example of each of the five syllable types presented in this book.

1. Closed _____   3. **Cle** _____   5. Double Vowel _____

2. Open _____   4. **VCe** _____

6 **Writing Words by Syllables.** Write the words that you hear one syllable at a time. Then write the whole word on the line at the right. Use the syllable types to help you spell the word.

First Syllable	Second Syllable	Third Syllable	Fourth Syllable	Whole Word
1. _____	_____	_____		_____
2. _____	_____	_____		_____
3. _____	_____	_____		_____
4. _____	_____	_____		_____
5. _____	_____	_____		_____
6. _____	_____	_____		_____
7. _____	_____	_____	_____	_____
8. _____	_____	_____	_____	_____

7 **Word Building.** Add a syllable from Column 2 to a syllable in Column 1 to make a word. Write the words on the lines provided. Use each syllable only once.

Column 1	Column 2	Words
sea	ley	1. _____
val	dy	2. _____
mud	son	3. _____
pre	ro	4. _____
he	fix	5. _____

8 **Using Irregular Verbs.** Fill in the blank in each sentence below with the correct form of the verb in parentheses.

1. (go)   Gail has _____ to the store to get some milk.

2. (hear)   Have you _____ the news about Joe's promotion?

3. (hide)   Amy can't remember where she _____ her diary.

4. (give)   Gary _____ Joan a ring for her birthday.

5. (mean)   Did you figure out what Lee _____ when he said that?

6. (strike) The car _____ the telephone pole, but no one was hurt.

7. (come)   Jean _____ to the apartment shortly after you left.

8. (know)   Steve has _____ Ray since they were in elementary school.

9. (speak)   Tony has _____ to the neighbors about the noise several times.

10. (eat)   I hope they haven't _____ all the cake by the time we get there.

9 **Reviewing Homonyms.** Write a sentence using each of the following homonyms.

1. hole   _____

2. whole   _____

3. meat   _____

4. meet   _____

5. plane   _____

6. plain   _____

7. steal   _____

8. steel   _____

9. waist   _____

10. waste   _____

Crossword Puzzle. Use the clues below to complete the puzzle. The answers are all word family or sight words from this text.

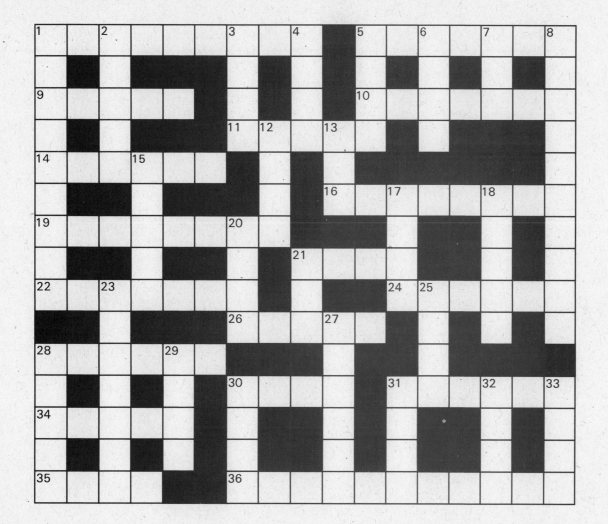

Across

1. The officer of a club who takes notes and keeps minutes
5. To answer
9. Selected
10. Not as dark
11. The day before tomorrow
14. To breathe in
16. The middle of the night
19. Opposite of decrease
21. Two nickles equals one _____.
22. To give reasons for
24. To give up one's job or position
26. Each
28. Mother or father
30. To appear to be
31. Homonym of throne
34. All by yourself
35. Always: forever and _____
36. The work of keeping something in good repair

Down

1. Give up: I decided to _____ my free weekend to help John move.
2. Material for making clothes
3. Your father's sister
4. Three feet
5. Depend on
6. A signal: a stop _____
7. Abbreviation for October
8. Instructions on how to do something
12. A woodwind instrument
13. A purpose or goal: His _____ is to pass this course.
15. The fourth month
17. An animal that lives in forests
18. The seed of a cereal plant such as wheat
20. Mentally healthy; sensible
21. To change the color of something
23. The reason for something: What is the _____ of this meeting?
25. Every

27. To stay in a place
28. This flies through the sky.
29. Require: I _____ eight hours of sleep.
30. A homonym for seem
31. A story: A fairy _____
32. The opposite of closed
33. This is in the middle of a face.

Word Families and Representative Words

Lesson 1

ake
awake
bake
baker
brake
brake fluid
cake
mistake
shake
snake
stake
take
wake

ame
became
blame
came
flame
frame
framed
name
same

ade
grade
lemonade
made
parade
shade
spade
trade
wade

ate
ate
exaggerate
fascinate
fate
gate
late
lately
later
locate
plate
state
United States

age
age
cage
engage
engagement
page
stage
teenager
wage

Lesson 2

ane
airplane
cane
insane
Jane
lane
mane
plane
sane
vane

ale
ale
female
inhale
male
pale
sale
salesperson
scale
tale

ave
behave
brave
cave
forgave
gave
grave
pave
save

afe
chafe
safe
safely
safety

aste
haste
paste
taste
waste

Lesson 3

ase
base
basement
case
chase
eraser
vase

ace
bracelet
disgrace
face
graceful
lace
misplace
pace
place
race
space
trace

aze
amaze
amazement
blaze
craze
daze
gaze
haze
maze

ange
arrange
change
danger
dangerous
exchange
range
strange
stranger

ape
cape
drape
escape
grape
scrape
scraper
shape
tape

Lesson 4

ail
ail
daily
detail
fail
Gail
mail
nail
pail
rail
railroad
retail
sail
sailor
tail
tailor
trail

aim
aim
aimless
claim
maim
reclaim

ain
complain
contain
entertainment
explain
gain
maintain
maintenance
obtain
pain
plain
rain
remain
retain
stain
strain
train

ait
bait
trait
wait
waiter

Lesson 5

aid
afraid
aid
braid
braided
laid
maid
paid
prepaid
raid

air
air
chair
fair
flair
hair
pair
repair
stairs

aise
appraisal
appraise
mayonnaise
praise
raise

aint
acquaint
acquaintance
complaint
faint
paint
restraint

Lesson 6

ay
anyway
away
day
delay
display
highway
okay
pay
payday
payment
play
portray
repay
say
stay
way

are
bare
care
fare
flare
rare
share

silverware
welfare

ary
imaginary
library
literary
necessary
primary
scary
secondary
solitary
temporary
vary
vocabulary
voluntary

azy
crazy
hazy
lazy

Lesson 7

e
be
being
beyond
ego
equal
he
legal
maybe
me
prefix
react
senior

ee
agree
bee
coffee
fee
flee
free
freedom
knee
needle
see
three
tree

eer
beer
cheer
deer
pioneer
steer
volunteer

Lesson 8

eek
cheek
creek
Greek
peek
seek
sleek
week
weekend

eel
feel
heel
kneel
peel
steel
wheel

eet
beet
feet
fleet
greet
meeting
sheet
sleet
sweet

eem
esteem
redeem
seem

Lesson 9

een
between
canteen
fifteen
fourteen
green
keen
queen
screen
seen
teen
teenager
thirteen

eed
agreed
bleed
deed
feed
greed
indeed
need
proceed
seed
speed
succeed
weed

eep
asleep
creep
deep
doorkeeper
jeep
keep
peep
sheep
sleep
steep
sweep
weep

eech
screech
speech
speechless

Lesson 10

ea
eager
measles
pea
plea
reason
sea
season
tea
teaspoon

ead
bead
lead
plead
read

eak
creak
leak
peak
sneakers
speak

squeak
streak
weak

eam
beam
cream
dream
scream
seam
steam
stream
team

Lesson 11

eat
beat
cheat
defeat
eat
heat
heater
meat
neat
repeat
seat
treat
wheat

eal
appeal
conceal
deal
heal
meal
real
reveal
seal
steal

ean
bean
clean
dean
Jean
lean
mean

eap
cheap
heap
leap

Lesson 12

each
beach

bleach
each
impeach
impeachment
peach
preach
reach
teach
teacher
unbleached

east
beast
east
feast
least

ear
appear
clear
dear
disappear
ear
fear
hear
near
rear
shears
weary
year

Lesson 13

eeze
breeze
freeze
sneeze
squeeze

ease
cease
crease
decrease
disease
displease
ease
grease
increase
please
release
tease

eave
heave
leave
leaves
weave

ceive
conceive
deceive
receive

Lesson 14

ey
hockey
honey
jersey
journey
key
kidney
money
monkey
valley
volleyball

y
any
bravery
greasy
greedy
icy
recovery
secretary
shady
sleepy
study
wavy

ly
daily
doubly
gently
jelly
lately
lonely
Molly
really
truly
ugly

Lesson 15

ime
chime
crime
dime
grime
overtime
prime
slime
sometimes
time

ibe
bribe
describe
prescribe
tribe

ike
alike
bike
dike
hike
like
Mike
spike
strike

ice
advice
device
ice
mice
nice
price
rice
sacrifice
slice
twice

ipe
gripe
pipeline
ripe
stripe
swipe
wipe

ile
awhile
file
meanwhile
mile
pile
smile
tile
while

Lesson 16

ine
combine
decline
define
dine
fine
line
mine
shine
spine

sunshine
Valentine
whine

ire
admire
bonfire
desire
entire
expire
fire
hire
inquire
require
retired
tire
wire

ide
beside
bride
decide
divide
hide
pride
provide
ride
side
slide
tide
wide

ite
bite
excite
excitement
ignite
invite
kite
quite
recite
unexcited
unite
white
write

ife
knife
life
lifetime
wife

ive
alive
drive
driveway
hive

live
thrive

Lesson 17

ise
advertise
advise
arise
despise
disguise
exercise
revise
rise
supervise
surprise
wise

ize
alphabetize
criticize
memorize
prize
realize
recognize
size

y
apply
cry
deny
dry
fry
identify
rely
reply
shy
supply
try
why

Lesson 18

ight
bright
delight
fight
flashlight
light
midnight
might
night
right
sight
tight
tonight

igh

highway
sigh
thigh

ign
align
assign
benign
design
resign
sign

ind
behind
bind
blind
find
kind
kindness
mind
remind

ild
child
grandchild
mild
wild

Lesson 19

ope
cope
envelope
hope
rope
slope
telescope

one
alone
bone
lone
lonely
phone
postpone
shone
stone
telephone
tone
zone

oke
broke
broken
joke
poke
provoke
revoke

smoke
spoke
stroke
woke

ome
dome
home
homeless
homesick
Nome
Rome

ove
cove
drove
grove
rove
strove
stove
stovepipe
wove

Lesson 20

obe
globe
lobe
probe
robe
strobe

ote
devote
note
notebook
quote
remote
vote
voter
wrote

ode
code
erode
explode
mode
rode
zip code

ore
before
chore
core
folklore
moreover
ore
restore

shore
shoreline
sore
store
tore

ose
chose
close
disclose
expose
hose
nose
pose
rose
suppose
those

oze
bulldozer
doze
froze
frozen

Lesson 21

ole
buttonhole
hole
keyhole
mole
parole
pole
role
sole
stole
whole
wholesale
wholesome

oll
enroll
knoll
poll
roll
stroll
swollen
toll
wholly

old
blindfold
bold
cold
golden
hold
scold
sold

told
withhold

olt
bolt
colt
jolted
revolt
voltage

Lesson 22

oat
boat
coat
float
gloat
oats
overcoat
sailboat
throat

oam
foam
roam
styrofoam

oal
charcoal
coal
field goal
goal

oad
carload
goad
load
railroad
road
toad

oan
groan
Joan
loan
moan

oak
cloak
croak
oak
soak

oast
boast
coast
coastal

coaster
coastline
roller coaster
roast
toast

oach
coach
cockroach
poached
stagecoach

Lesson 23

o
ago
donate
go
local
locate
obey
ocean
omit
over
piano
program
radio
so
sofa
solo
Soviet

oe
doe
foe
goes
hoe
Joe
oboe
tiptoe
toe
woe

ow
below
blow
borrow
crow
elbow
grow
know
low
narrow
overflow
rainbow
row
shadow
show

slowly
snowflake
throw
tomorrow
tow
window

own
blown
flown
grown
known
own
ownership
shown
thrown

Sight Words

Sight Word	Lesson Number	Sight Word	Lesson Number	Sight Word	Lesson Number	Sight Word	Lesson Number
add	5	especially	7	ounce	17	west	3
all right	19	every	5	owe	10	western	3
almost	19	faith	5	oz.	17	wolf	11
already	19	father	14	parent	14	woman	20
although	9	February	1	people	4	women	20
altogether	18	ferry	6	person	4	worry	20
always	19	find	4	pound	17	yard	22
answer	15	flood	8	pretty	5	young	13
April	1	floor	18	promise	21		
August	2	fluid	17	prove	7		
aunt	14	foot	22	purpose	11		
beauty	5	group	16	question	15		
beef	8	half	8	ready	19		
been	12	heart	8	rhyme	15		
berry	6	hero	13	rough	9		
blood	8	how	23	route	16		
board	15	howl	23	September	2		
bored	15	hurry	20	shoulder	16		
both	15	husband	20	skiing	21		
broad	12	inch	22	sleeve	13		
bury	11	January	1	soul	21		
busy	11	July	2	south	3		
calf	8	June	1	southern	3		
canoe	21	kilometer	22	special	7		
carry	6	lb.	17	spirit	21		
centimeter	22	leaf	12	spouse	20		
cheese	13	leash	12	straight	18		
cloth	21	length	7	strength	7		
clothes	12	liquid	17	style	18		
clown	23	loose	4	sugar	11		
coarse	10	lose	4	suppose	11		
color	11	machine	12	talk	4		
cough	16	many	12	teeth	8		
country	13	March	1	terrible	18		
couple	14	marry	6	thorough	16		
course	10	material	12	though	9		
court	16	May	1	tight	4		
cousin	14	merry	6	tongue	8		
December	2	meter	22	touch	13		
die	15	most	19	tough	9		
direction	5	moth	21	towel	23		
door	18	mother	14	town	23		
double	10	move	7	trouble	10		
dough	9	north	3	type	18		
during	21	northern	3	usual	18		
dye	15	November	2	very	6		
east	3	now	23	waist	5		
eastern	3	October	2	walk	4		
else	11	odd	5	weigh	17		
enough	9	oh	10	weight	17		

Glossary of Terms

affix   A word element which carries meaning and is attached to a root word. Prefixes and suffixes are affixes; for example, *de-* and *-ful* in *delightful*.

blend   The joining together of two or more sounds with each sound still being heard; for example. /tr/ in *trade*.

C   A symbol representing any consonant.

compound word   A word formed by combining two or more words. Compound words can be closed (*greenhouse*), hyphenated (*red-letter*), or open (*yellow jacket*).

diacritical mark   A mark added to a letter to show how to pronounce the letter; for example, the straight line over a vowel to show a long vowel sound.

diagraph   A pair of letters which represent one sound; for example, *ch* making the sound /ch/ in *chain* and *ea* making the sound /ē/ in *sea*.

family   A letter pattern or sequence such as *ine* in *fine, mine*, and *combine*. The pattern usually forms a common syllable ending and is composed of a vowel or vowel combination plus the consonant(s) that go with it.

homonym   One of a pair or more of words having the same sound but different meanings and often different spellings, for example, *tail* and *tale*.

pattern   A recurrent, usually predictable sequence of letters. Patterns occur in common syllables (e.g., *ope*) as well as in prefixes, suffixes, roots, and compound words. Spelling rules also produce patterns.

prefix   A word element which carries meaning and is attached to the beginning of a root word; for example, *pre-* in *prepaid*.

schwa   A vowel sound that usually occurs in unstressed syllables in English as heard in the first syllable of *against*; also the symbol (ə) often used to represent the sound.

sight word   A word which is not phonetically predictable; also any word for which students have not had the phonics to enable them to spell the word phonetically.

suffix   A word element which carries meaning and is attached to the end of a root word; for example, *-less* in *speechless*.

syllable   A spoken unit of uninterrupted sound containing one vowel sound producing either a word (e.g., *pay*) or a distinct part of a word (e.g., *pay* or *ment* in *payment*); the letters producing that sound in the word.

V   A symbol representing any vowel.

Style Notes

/x/ A letter between slashes indicates a sound rather than a spelling; for instance /b/ is the sound produced by the letter *b*.

/ĭ/ A curved mark (breve) over a vowel indicates the short vowel sound.

/ī/ A straight line (macron) over a vowel indicates the long vowel sound.

/ə/ This indicates the schwa sound.